Pills, Shills, and the Psychiatry Wars: Musings from the Drug Safety & Health News Blog (Book 2 in a Series)

Doug Bremner

Pills, Shills, and the Psychiatry Wars: Musings from the Drug Safety & Healthcare News Blog (Book 2 in a Series)

Printed in the United States of America

First Printing December 2023

Laughing Cow Books

ISBN: 978-0-9995499-7-1

Books by Doug Bremner

Does Stress Damage the Brain? Understanding Trauma-Related Disorders from a Mind-Body Perspective W.W. Norton & Co. (2002)

Brain Imaging Handbook W.W. Norton & Co. (2005)

Before You Take That Pill: Why the Drug Industry May Be Bad for your Health: Risks and Side Effects You Won't Find on the Label of Commonly Prescribed Drugs, Vitamins and Supplements Penguin/Avery (2008)

A Fresh Look at Greed Laughing Cow Books (2013)

The Fastest Growing Religion on Earth: How Genealogy Captured the Brains and Imaginations of Americans Laughing Cow Books (2013)

You Can't Just Snap Out of It: The Real Path to Recovery from Psychological Trauma Laughing Cow Books (2014)

History of the Bremner Family: The Story of John Bremner of Aberdeenshire, Scotland, and his

Descendants in America Laughing Cow Books (2014)

The Goose that Laid the Golden Egg: Accutane, the truth that had to be told. Laughing Cow Books, 2nd edition (2018)

The Moon Had No Compassion for the Dead, and other Poems Laughing Cow Books (2018)

Justice in the Age of Judgment: From Amanda Knox to Kyle Rittenhouse and the Battle for Due Process in the Digital Age (with Anne Bremner) Skyhorse Publishing (2022)

Pimps, Whores, & Chiggers: Musings from the Drug Safety & Health News Blog: The Corrupting Influence of Big Pharma Laughing Cow Books (2023)

Edited books:

Trauma, Memory, and Dissociation (with Charles Marmar) American Psychiatric Press (1998)

Posttraumatic Stress Disorder: A Comprehensive Text (with Philip Saigh) Allyn & Bacon (1999)

Posttraumatic Stress Disorder: From Neurobiology to Treatment Wiley (2016).

Films:

Inheritance, Italian Style Laughing Cow Productions (2021)

His personal website is at dougbremner.com.

Pills, Shills, and the Psychiatry Wars

This book is dedicated to my wife, Viola Vaccarino, M.D., Ph.D., known herein as "Mrs. Bremner."

Table of Contents

Pills, Shills, and the Psychiatry Wars

Introduction

This book is the second of a series that comes out of my writings on the internet and follows *Pimps, Whores, and Chiggers: Musings from the Drug Safety and Health News Blog: The Corrupting Influence of Big Pharma*. Originally, I started writing on the *Drug Safety and Health News Blog* in 2008 at the urging of my editors from Avery / Penguin, to promote my new book *Before You Take That Pill: Why the Drug Industry May Be Bad For Your Health: Risks and Side Effects You Won't Find on the Labels of Commonly Prescribed Drugs, Vitamins, and Supplements*.

My book, *Does Stress Damage the Brain? Understanding Trauma-Based Disorders from a Mind-Body Perspective*, published in 2002 by WW Norton, highlighted my thesis that certain psychiatric disorders, what I called trauma-spectrum disorders, and which included posttraumatic stress disorder (PTSD), borderline personality disorder (BPD), and some cases of substance use disorders and depression, shared a link in having an etiology related to childhood trauma. We were able to show that all of the disorders, when associated with a history of childhood trauma, shared a common neurobiological underpinning, a reduction in volume of a brain area involved in memory called the hippocampus, that could be seen on magnetic resonance imaging (MRI). At the time, PTSD was grouped with other "Anxiety Disorders" including Panic Disorder and Obsessive-Compulsive Disorder. We showed that these disorders didn't share the trademark signature of smaller hippocampal volume, and therefore PTSD, although it was associated with anxiety, did not belong in the Anxiety Disorders classification. It was later moved out of that category, to what degree that was related to my writings, I don't know.

Does Stress Damage the Brain? was published as a "professional" book by WW Norton, and I decided that I would like to write a book about psychological trauma for people suffering from the effects of psychological trauma. That led to *You Can't Just Snap Out of It*. My agent shopped the rounds of the New York publishing companies with our proposal, but they weren't interested, saying that they were ready to "move on" from the trauma of the September 11, 2001, attack on the World Trade Center in New York City. I later published the book through a small publisher. But as I was having lunch with my agents in New York, I talked about my work as an expert witness related to the acne medication, Accutane, which led to a larger review of all medications, vitamins, and supplements, published by Penguin in 2008 as *Before You Take That Pill*. I blogged about the pharmaceutical industry and news related to medications and healthcare in general, which is the basis of the first book in this series, *Pimps, Whores, and Chiggers: Musings from the Drug Safety and Health News Blog: The Corrupting Influence of Big Pharma*, which were a series of posts from my blog as well as my writings for *The Huffington Post*. Postings about the pharmaceutical industry continued, but were interwoven with posts about my own field of psychiatry, and controversies over changes in psychiatric diagnosis with the development of the Diagnostic and Statistical Manual-5 (DSM-5). This was naturally related to the pharmaceutical industry, because drug companies were using diagnostic nomenclature as a vehicle to boost sales of their drugs.

My experiences in getting "discovery," where you see the internal emails and memos that go on behind closed doors at a drug company, and how they try to spin their drugs, putting profits over people, had made me angry. The Hoffmann La Roche Pharmaceutical Company called Accutane their Goose that Laid Golden Eggs, because it just kept making money for them, with little effort on their part. But they had to protect their golden goose, which meant attacking the credibility and ruining the career of what they perceived as the primary threat to their golden goose, which was me based on my research that the drug affected a part of the brain called the orbitofrontal cortex that was known to be involved in depression. Roche's strategy was to beat me down and discredit my research, to the point of accusing me of fraud to my university and the National Institutes of Health Office of Research Integrity in an attempt to get me fired and my research funding pulled. I was deposed for eight hours a day over 14 times, which led to my blog post *Deposition X*, in the prior volume of this series, in which I wrote about how I didn't want to count the number of times I'd been deposed, as the 13th one would be an unlucky one. I wrote about my experience as an expert witness in the Accutane litigation in *The Goose That Laid the Golden Egg: Accutane, the truth that had to be told.*

As I was going through the Accutane litigation, I started to look back on my own life, which led to questions about my childhood. My mother died suddenly when I was four years old. I wrote about my search for the family of my mother, who was adopted, in *The Fastest Growing Religion on Earth.* Posts related to this process of discovery about my past are interwoven in the current book with posts about healthcare and the psychiatry field, *Pills, Shills, and the Psychiatry Wars: Musings from the Drug Safety &Health News Blog (Book 2 in a Series).* Shills refers to people who promote the... pills... usually for personal profit. Chiggers are a small insect from the forests of Georgia that get under your skin (literally).

Anyway, I leave you with the second in the series of my writings from the *Pimps, Whores, and Chiggers* series, *Pills, Shills, and the Psychiatry Wars: Musings from the Drug Safety and Health News Blog.* I hope you enjoy!

Chapter 1: No Redemption for Preemption

(Originally posted October 3, 2008, in *The Huffington Post*).

While Americans sit mesmerized by Sarah Palin clapping into the microphone and rambling on about Greek Columns while her daughter wipes down her youngest child's hair with her own spit, they are utterly unaware of yet another attempt by the Republican machine to steal even more of their civil rights and liberties. As if the "Patriot" Act wasn't enough, the war mongerers now want to take away your civil rights in the form of redress in the event that you or your family are damaged by dangerous prescription drugs. And while the fear mongerers are hyping the "War on Drugs" and making chemical attacks against Columbian farmers, they aren't drawing attention to the fact that three times as many people die from "legal" prescription medications every year as from illegal drugs, and that the government is getting ready to remove your right to have any recourse for the harm that is done to you by a pharmaceutical company.

That's right, "preemption" is coming soon to a theater near you. Preemption states that if a drug is approved by the Food and Drug Administration (FDA), that approval "preempts" the rights of citizens to litigate in state courts. The good people of Michigan have been living with this ludicrous law for the past decade. People from Michigan who had a heart attack on Vioxx lost their right to have their day in court. That is because preemption says that "if the FDA approved it, it is OK," ignoring the fact that scientists have been saying that Vioxx causes heart attacks since 2000, and the FDA literally had to be beaten over the head before they came along six years later. Ditto for suicidality with antidepressants; it took a strong stance by the British organization for the regulation of prescription medications before the FDA "reopened" their files and changed their opinion on the issue. In the case of Levine v. Wyeth Pharmaceuticals, involving a musician who lost her right arm as a consequence of a medication administered to her for migraine headaches in an emergency room, the US Supreme Court will soon rule on whether FDA approval "preempts" the rights of citizens to receive any form of redress in state courts.

Prescription medications are often found to have dangerous side effects after they are approved by the FDA. That is because it takes time and the treatment of many patients before uncommon, but potentially dangerous, side effects come to light. Even members of the FDA don't want preemption; they see civil litigation as complementary to the FDA. Since the passage of the Prescription Drug User Fee Act (PDUFA) in 1992, a law that allowed drug companies to pay a fee to the FDA to speed up the approval process, there has been a decline in the resources that the FDA has to monitor drugs after approval. That is because PDUFA requires a 3% yearly increase in the budget for new drug approval. Since Congress hasn't increased the FDA budget, that means the money went from monitoring approved drugs to approving new drugs.

Preemption isn't good for anyone except for the drug companies. And they are unable to come up with a coherent reason to be in favor of it, other than it will provide more money to develop "lifesaving drugs," and we've heard that malarkey before. If you are tired of the erosion of your rights as a US citizen, take action.

Chapter 2: The Press Release that was Never... Released

(Originally posted October 10, 2008, in *Drug Safety & Health News*).

In March of 2008 my book, *Before You Take That Pill: Why The Drug Industry May Be Bad For Your Health* was published by Avery/Penguin. Having a book published is sort of like giving birth to a child. There is all sorts of excitement leading up to it, etc. Part of the excitement is working with the public relations department of your university to come up with ways to pitch it to reviewers and getting it noticed, including writing the press release.

That is why I was justifiably disturbed when on publication day I scanned the internet looking for the Emory press release and couldn't find it. So, I called the public relations person and asked where it was.

"We decided not to release it," she said.

"Why not?" I asked.

"Because we felt that your publisher was doing a good enough job on that already."

Well, that was highly unusual for Emory, who has a supercharged PR department. Most authors get press releases, their own web page for their book, the works. Besides, they had already written it. Why not go ahead and release it? I got the impression that they didn't want PR for that book, they hoped it would be ignored, because they didn't want to piss off the pharma industry.

Given how things have gone this week for their PR, I think they made a mistake in not issuing my press release.[1] But hey, what do I know.

Anyway, here is the press release that was never... released (sniff, sniff)

The Missing Press Release

DRAFT COPY

EMORY Health Sciences News

http://www.whsc.emory.edu

XXX, 2008

Medications Put to the Test in New Book by Emory Researcher and Author

Media contacts:

Kathi Baker, 404/727-9371, kobaker@emory.edu

Sarah Goodwin, 404/727-3366, sgoodwi@emory.edu

ATLANTA J. Douglas Bremner, M.D., an Emory University and Atlanta Veterans Affairs Medical Center researcher, was concerned about the way information was communicated about medications and supplements, so he decided to take action. After two years of doing his own research on hundreds of the most popular medications, he has written a book called "Before You Take that Pill," which is scheduled to be released on February 28, 2008.

"You have the right to know the risks and benefits of the pills you take and to form an active partnership with your doctor to make decisions about what is right for you," says Dr. Bremner.

"We all want to live as long as possible," he continues. "If this book allows you to use medications safely and convinces you to change your diet and lifestyle to prevent disease, I will consider it a success."

The book covers over 300 of the most commonly prescribed prescription drugs, the fifty top-selling prescription drugs, vitamins, and the best-selling herbs and supplements. Also included in the book are drugs that are not used much anymore but that are particularly unsafe and haven't been taken off the market yet by the Food and Drug Administration (FDA).

Dr. Bremner says the U.S. is focused on developing newer drugs. But those drugs are more expensive and drive-up health care costs and are not necessarily more effective than the older drugs. He says that pharmaceutical companies are not required to prove that new drugs are better and have fewer side effects than the older drugs they are claiming to replace.

In addition to that, vitamins and supplements and some medications can be avoided altogether if people are encouraged to stick with a healthy diet, exercise regularly and wash their hands to avoid infection.

"Despite the fact that Americans spend twice as much on health care as any other country in the world, we have some of the worst health care outcomes," says Dr. Bremner. "In a survey of 13 industrialized nations, the United States was found to be the last in many health-related measures, and overall was second to the last!"

Dr. Bremner read and analyzed journal articles, editorials, and drug research related to all the medications he describes in this book. Additionally, he reviewed investigative reporting about the safety of the drugs in credible publications such as *The New York Times*, and he consulted colleagues with specialties related to the medication he was researching.

Says Dr. Bremner "My goal in writing this book is to give patients all the information they need to be aware of the effects of the medications they are taking so that they can have knowledgeable conversations with their physicians and make informed decisions together."

Dr. Bremner is professor of Psychiatry and Radiology at Emory University School of Medicine, director of the Emory Clinical Neuroscience Research Unit and director of Mental Health Research, Atlanta Veterans Affairs Medical Center. Dr. Bremner performs research using brain imaging to look at the effects of medications on the brain and brain correlates of mental disorders. He is a board-certified psychiatrist and nuclear medicine physician and has authored or co-authored over 200 peer reviewed articles and book chapters and three books, including "Before You Take that Pill."

####

Chapter 3: Can You Please Put Some Sugar on This Crap?

I guess someone told Fox that they are getting a lot of advertising dollars from the pharmaceutical industry, and what I had to say might not make some people happy.

By **Doug Bremner, Contributor**

(Originally posted Oct 13, 2008, in *The Huffington Post*).

I had some time I didn't expect to have yesterday since my anticipated appearance on Fox's *Mike and Juliet Show* to talk about the link between the acne medication Accutane (isotretinoin) and depression and suicide was canceled, so I thought I'd write about how my day was going so far. I guess someone told Fox that they are getting a lot of advertising dollars from the pharmaceutical industry, and what I had to say might not make some people happy. At first, they asked if I would like to go on the show and "debate" someone. When I didn't seem too excited about that they said they would "get back to me" and then later left me a voice message saying that I wouldn't be going on the show but that I would be "credited" for my work. So I checked out the clip on the internet, and low and behold Fox set up the story by starting out with a family's complaints about Accutane causing their son to commit suicide, followed by an attractive dermatologist named Cheryl Karcher, MD, who sat there in her white coat and said "I'm soooo sorry for the Zimmers but there is no evidence that Accutane causes depression or suicide."

Cheryl Karcher, M.D.

Well, I thought to myself "who the hell is this person?" I mean, she didn't even offer any reasons for her opinion, and we are just expected to sit back there and say "OK!" Was she a researcher? What was the basis for her opinion? I asked myself. So, I looked up her bio on the internet and found that she was a "nationally recognized expert" whose qualifications included acting as a consultant to the

Miss Universe Contest! The bio went on to state that "Articles detailing the results of Dr. Karcher's research have been published in numerous peer-reviewed scientific journals including *The New England Journal of Medicine*, *The Journal of Investigative Dermatology*, and *The Journal of the American Academy of Dermatology*." Well, I looked her up on PubMed, and I couldn't find any articles that she had written. Then I realized that by saying "results of her research" might indicate that she was part of a clinical trial but wasn't listed as an author of the paper.

Like the 5,000 authors of the Advantage Trial of Vioxx? Pretty misleading!

Next FOX-y Juliet said, "after the break, see pictures of what your brain looks like on Accutane." Well, I thought, that's great, maybe we'll get a little more balance in this story. Little did I know that the worst was yet to come. After showing images of my brain scans showing how Accutane is associated with a decrease in function of the frontal lobe, a part of the brain that regulates emotion, they had a psychiatrist named Petros Levounis, MD, come on the show and state that yes, Accutane changes your brain function, "but I 100% agree with Dr. Karcher that there is no evidence that Accutane causes depression or suicide." Again, stated with absolutely no reason for his opinion! A quick check of Dr. Levounis's profile showed four publications, none of which were about Accutane.

I mean, viewers are supposed to look at the victim family and look at the doctor and say "OK, poor family but the doctor says there's nothing there, so I'll believe the doctor."

I have presented the evidence elsewhere that Accutane is associated with depression and suicide. So, if people want, they can go read it themselves. I have never met anyone who wasn't on the payroll for Roche who has read the evidence who doesn't agree, and I have never met any dermatologist who could look me in the eye and tell me that she never had a patient become depressed or feel like they were in a haze while on Accutane.

So, there you have it, folks. Out-FOXed again. That is how the media presents things to you. Nothing is ever "proven" and there are always two viewpoints that balance each other out.

So, the next time you turn on your tube to feed yourself, why don't you send FOX an email asking, "Can you put some sugar on that crap you're feeding me?"

I guess we got it, sort of, with Dr. Karcher.

Now read online, "Exercise Better Than Drugs for Depression."[2]

[Update] I no longer can say that I haven't met a dermatologist not on Roche's payroll who denies that Accutane can cause depression. Social media is now rampant with them, what I call the TikTok Dermatologists. I therefore created several videos on TikTok to counter them @jamesdouglasbremner.

Chapter 4: We Come in Peas

(Originally posted October 14, 2008, in *Drug Safety & Health News*).

I wanted to let everyone know that today is a special day.

It was announced several months ago that on today, October 14, 2008, an 800-mile-long space craft will appear above the United States and hover there for two to three days.

There are a number of videos circulating on Youtube about the event.

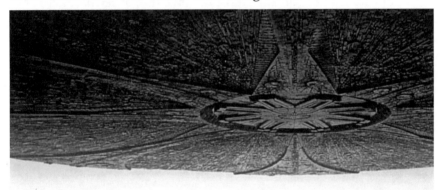

Spaceship (Source: 20th Century Fox)

Apparently, they are coming in such a large ship so that the mainstream media and government won't be able to cover up their appearance. Because if you show up in an 800-mile-long spaceship--that's kind of hard to keep secret, don't you think?

They are apparently coming in peace in order to demonstrate to us that they exist but are using such a large ship so that there will be no way for the government or the media to conceal their appearance. Many new age people (see below) feel that the arrival of the aliens will coincide with a higher level of consciousness which includes peace with others and a respect of the earth, including preserving the environment.

Our family, largely spurred by our daughter Sabina, has been trying to improve our footprint on the earth. We collect water in buckets while waiting for the water to get hot in the shower (we have a drought in Atlanta, GA), we put our vegetable refuse in a compost pile, and we recycle. In the future we will try and use solar and other similar types of power.

We also get our vegetables from a local community supported agriculture (CSA) group, which means we pay a local network of Georgia farmers to drop off whatever vegetables they have grown that week where we pick it up. We eat whatever is growing in Georgia that week to avoid the carbon footprint of buying vegetables from Argentina, or where-ever. Another one of my daughter's ideas.

Which brings me to my next point.

We come in peas.

An old friend of my mother's who was moved by a memorial service we had for my mom last week who died in 1966 wrote to inform me that our service indeed signified spiritual healing and he implied that it was a sign of better things to come.

Doug Bremner and Lynn Dickerson standing by the gravestone of their mother in Tumwater, Washington

I think my mom would like my daughter Sabina.

You see, many people with so-called New Age beliefs think that we are moving toward a better time in our society when people will be able to abandon war and conflict and live together in harmony.

I could live with that!

I'd even be willing to give up my Veterans Administration and Department of Defense research grants on posttraumatic stress disorder (PTSD) related to Iraq combat for that!

Many thought the better time would happen in 1987, when there would be a so-called cosmic convergence. A lot of people "converged" on places like Stonehenge and Sedona, Arizona, where there are special vortexes and other things that permit connections with other dimensions.

As seen by President Bush's invasion of Iraq, they were not completely successful.

New Age believers also look to the Mayan calendar which combines calendars of 260 and 365 days into a cycle of so called Haabs, that represent a cyclical turning of time. The Mayan calendar will end on December 12, 2012, following which the universe will presumably be sucked away like something being dragged into a cosmic toilet.

Many New Age believers look to various events as signifying the arrival of the new age.

The psychic, Dr. Ralph Duby, apparently "channeled" some information from a cosmic source regarding the passing of my mother back in 1966.

But I'm not going to tell you what it was.

Ha ha ha ha ha!

I am glad to learn, however, that the ceremony for her is ushering in a better age when we may perhaps be able to better live with people from other galaxies.

After all, our son does meet criteria for an Indigo Child.

And when he was a child, we called him a "chip from outer space."

Coincidence? Space child? Who knows.

However, the Youtube sources say that the spaceship will arrive in Alabama. We have some sources on our *Drug Safety and Health News* blog network (you know who you are girls) so I am sending out an urgent appeal.

When the spaceship appears, since the government will likely jam all sources of communication, will you get on your ponies and ride over to Georgia and give us the warning?

Chapter 5: Don't Panic! Keep Taking Your Vytorin! (I Mean Aspirin!)

(Originally posted October 17, 2008, in *Drug Safety & Health News*).

A study in the *British Medical Journal* published today showed that aspirin confers no benefit in the prevention of heart attack or stroke, and may increase the risk of bleeding, in patients with diabetes (who are considered at "hi-risk" for these problems).

The prevention of progression of arterial disease and diabetes (POPADAD) trial involved 1276 adults over age 40 with diabetes from 16 hospitals in Scotland.[3] Primary outcome was heart attack or stroke (fatal or non-fatal) or amputation because of ischemia. Patients were treated with four variations of combinations of aspirin, antioxidant pills, or placebo. The antioxidant capsule contained alpha-tocopherol 200 mg, ascorbic acid 100 mg, pyridoxine hydrochloride 25 mg, zinc sulphate 10 mg, nicotinamide 10 mg, lecithin 9.4 mg, and sodium selenite 0.8 mg. There were no differences in the primary end point between those treated with aspirin plus antioxidant (58) (18%), aspirin plus placebo 59 (18%), placebo plus antioxidant (59) (18%), or placebo plus placebo (58) (18%), p value=0.92. People who took antioxidants actually had higher mortality, about 23%, compared to those who didn't at about 16%. More people who took aspirin (57) had gastrointestinal bleeding than those who did not (45), difference that was not statistically significant.

The dismal results of this study did not stop a doctor from saying "Don't panic and don't stop taking your aspirin!"[4]

Kind of reminds me of the doc who said "Don't stop taking your..." You've got it. But we know who he was working for (see "Zeta, Schmetia").

POPADAD... I wonder who came up with the name of that one anyway. Did you know that they make up the names of the trials, and then try and come up with words that make sense to fit into the initials? But POPADAD is a good one. It's even better than VIGOR or ENHANCE. Kind of like "who's your daddy?" Maybe... the vitamin manufacturer?

Anyhoo, POPADAD's results are yet more news that antioxidant vitamins are not helpful and actually increase the risk of mortality as I have written about before (see, "Vitamins That Kill"). I have also warned people that the risk of bleeding outweighs the benefit of heart attack prevention for people without heart disease who take a daily aspirin.

Now read online, "Probiotics for Bowel Conditions: Is There Any Evidence They Are Helpful?"[5]

Chapter 6: What Me Worry? The FDA Will Protect Me From Toxic Drugs (Not!)

(Originally posted October 21, 2008, in *Drug Safety & Health News*).

Our Commander-in-Chief

Tomorrow's issue of *JAMA* has the results of an interesting study by T.J. Giezen et al that examined 174 prescription medications (136 in the US, the rest in Europe, and 67 approved in both places),[6] as well as some letters on preemption and an editorial that discusses these related topics. In the study of Giezen et al, 24% of the drugs had a regulatory action after approval by the FDA or a European regulatory agency, including 19 black box warnings, and 47 dear doctor letters. The probability of having regulatory action in the ten years after approval was 29%. Drugs that were the first of their kind ("first in class") had a four-fold higher risk of safety regulatory action than drugs that came on the market later.

Would you play Russian roulette with a four-chamber gun and a single bullet in the gun? I wouldn't. That is why the looming probability that preemption of tort litigation, which translates into English as citizens giving up their right to have a day in court for toxicity or death related to FDA prescription drugs, will become the law of the land, is particularly chilling. You see, the study by Giezen et al showed that one in four drugs are found to have a dangerous side effect, like cancer, or impairment of the immune system that can lead to life threatening infections after they have been on the market and approved by the FDA that wasn't known about before they were approved by the FDA.

It just isn't possible to know all of the possible side effects of medications with the small numbers of subjects that are included in studies leading up to the FDA approval process. The FDA itself admits that.

Which gets me to another topic that I have been harping about lately, preemption, and the case of Levine v Wyeth, which would take away the rights of citizens to have their day in court for damage caused to them by FDA approved prescription drugs. (See "No Redemption for Preemption" and "Some of Us Doctors Actually Care About Our Patients").

In a pair of letters, Piwinski and Fitpatrick initially assert that the case of Riegel v Medtronic Inc., in which the Supreme Court ruled that for medical devices that approval by the FDA preempted state law and eliminated the rights of citizens to have a day in court, was a good thing, that we shouldn't have juries and the right to trial [causing Jefferson and Madison to toss in their graves, surely] and that [in that particular case] the problem was not that Medtronic made a lousy angioplasty device that exploded in the coronary artery of the injured party, but that the guy had led a life of license or had a star crossed destiny that led to his demise. Gostin replied that juries do not evaluate medical devices, they listen to medical experts, and that we shouldn't be ready to toss the constitution just yet.

In an editorial on these letters and the study of Giezen et al, DeAngelis and Fontanaros cite the Institute of Medicine and FDA blue ribbon commission reports that noted that the FDA was woefully inadequate to protect us from toxic side effects, and was putting Americans at risk.[7] They said that post approval the drugs are used in populations that are less carefully selected than participants in clinical trials. [translation: the clinical trials pick squeaky clean participants that are least likely to have a bad reaction, viz Chantix for stop smoking trial excluded patients with mental disorders, who make up one fourth of the population and are twice as likely to smoke. They then cut loose the drug on the population and were surprised when people started freaking out on the drug]. See "Time To Die! (Oops) I Mean Time to Quit!"

DeAngelis and Fontanaros later write:

> Tort law serves in effect as a way to close regulatory
> gaps in the FDA premarketing approval process and to
> provide a mechanism for post-marketing surveillance.
> Moreover, litigation has been a rich source of
> information about how drug and device manufacturing
> companies behave, such as with off-label promotion,
> guest and ghost authorship, and reporting of safety
> findings. Without the information revealed by the
> public release of documents in tort liability actions,
> many of these behaviors would remain unknown, some
> drug manufacturers judgments about safety issues
> would be hidden from view, review, or oversight, and
> the FDA would not be able to uncover them either.

In other words, lawsuits are the only way to keep the bastards honest.

Catherine DeAngelis is probably still pissed off about the CLASS study of Celebrex (celecoxib) that was published in JAMA when she was the editor, in which the authors withheld data from the second six months of the study during which time Celebrex patients were shown to have an increase in heart attacks (see "Celebrex Increases the Risk of Cardiovascular Disease (Don't Let Them Tell You Otherwise" in the first volume of this series).

That, my friends, is fraudulent.

But it isn't clear that it would get snagged if preemption became the law of the land.

They further state that:

> ...drug manufacturers have the authority and responsibility to modify labeling when hazards manifest and may do so without securing prior approval from the FDA... The human body is in a constant state of change and the effects of some drugs will manifest only after exposure over time. Furthermore, some serious adverse drug effects are quite uncommon and require use of the drug in large numbers of patients to become evident. The safety of drugs in a clinical trial, the study type used for FDA approval, is based on specific participant types, numbers, and design that cannot ensure the true safety of a drug. In addition, manipulation of study results by the drug manufacturers (who almost always sponsor studies used for decisions about drug approval) can obscure the true safety profile of a drug... Therefore, unless and until the FDA drug approval process and the post-marketing surveillance system improve significantly, patients must have a means to seek recourse through tort litigation against product manufacturers. Anything less may well preempt the well-being and safety of the public.

In other words, the argument that the FDA alone decides what is a risky side effect, and that drug makers can't do anything without FDA approval, is poppycock.

I couldn't agree more.

Pay attention guys. This isn't just some bozo talking. This is from someone who has served as the editor of *JAMA*, one of the leading journals in the medical field.

Chapter 7: Health News You Won't Read About in *The New York Times*

Here's a forgotten chapter from pharmaceutical history. The acne drug, Accutane, manufactured by Roche Pharmaceuticals, has been associated with hundreds of birth defects.

By Doug Bremner, Contributor

(Originally posted October 30, 2008, in *The Huffington Post*).

Here's a forgotten chapter from pharmaceutical history. The acne drug, Accutane (isotretinoin), manufactured by Roche Pharmaceuticals, has been associated with hundreds of birth defects. Since 2005 the iPLEDGE program has required that patients, doctors, and pharmacists register and that patients prove they are on birth control before they can be prescribed this potentially dangerous drug. But it wasn't always that way.

Accutane was initially listed as a category C drug for risk of birth defects, meaning that it was only of moderate risk. Moderate risk means that there are some studies in animals showing birth defects, but it isn't clear that it is really relevant to humans. When Accutane came out on the American market, after being rushed through the FDA approval process, the PDR said only that women "should not" get pregnant while on Accutane. There was no requirement that doctors test for pregnancy, or that women take birth control.

Accutane hit the market and was hailed as a wonder drug. Sales soared far beyond the wildest expectations of Roche executives. Soon every girl with pimples was demanding that pill that her schoolmate got that had made her blemishes vanish away.

But not everyone was so sanguine. The Europeans weren't impressed by Accutane. It was banned in Sweden and Italy and sharply curtailed in other countries, because of the risk of birth defects associated with the use of Accutane.

If there were any birth defects in the European trials, were they reported to the FDA?

Nobody seems to remember. Hmm...

Over a decade ago in a newspaper called the Columbus (Ohio) Dispatch, Mark Somerson reported on this story in a series of investigative journalism articles. Remarkably this story about a drug that was equally dangerous as thalidomide never made it beyond the shores of the Wabash River.

Thanks, *The New York Times!*

Here's a scoop for you guys, Mike and Juliet, to add to your ongoing Accutane 'investigations'! (see "Can You Please Put Some Sugar on this Crap?")

It wasn't only the Europeans that were wary of Accutane. Some American dermatologists were as well. In fact, Frank W Yoder, MD, who with Greg Peck, M.D., was the first to report on the use of isotretinoin for the treatment of acne in 1979,[8] long before Roche picked it up, warned against the dangers of the drug in the January 1983 edition of the *Journal of the American Medical Association,* saying that "the potential toxicity of this drug has been seriously underemphasized."[9] Both American doctors and scientists working for Roche later testified that is was known before it came out on the market that Accutane potentially had a very dangerous risk of birth defects, based on the fact that it was derived from Vitamin A related compounds, well known for many years to cause birth defects in women. Yoder and another doctor involved in the US trials remembered discussing birth defects that occurred during the European trials, although exact names of individuals involved were never produced.

In fact, Roche had known about Accutane for years before the American dermatologists had written about it but did nothing with the drug. Somerson reported that Dr Werner Bollage, a scientist with the company, wrote in 1971 that it was "inconceivable to develop an agent" that caused birth defects for such a "common complaint as acne."

For their US clinical trial in the early 1980s, Roche required that all women get tested for pregnancy, and one woman who got pregnant was advised to get an abortion. However, once the drug went on the market, this was no longer required, according to reporting by Somerson.

Henry H. Roenigk, M.D., another dermatologist who had been involved in the US Accutane trial, was quoted as saying that he published a letter in the May 1982 edition of the journal Dermatology warning of the risk of birth defects and stating that there had already been birth defects with Accutane (presumably in Europe). Following this Roche wrote a letter to all doctors who had been involved in the US trial and told them not to "divulge trade secrets."

Nine months after Accutane went on the market in May 1982, babies with birth defects started to appear.

On Sept 8, 1983, after the first US birth defect cases were reported, Health Research Group wrote to the FDA urging them to require pregnancy tests and not to bury the warnings about birth defects in the "fine print" at the end of the product labeling.

By 1988 the FDA estimated there could be as many as 1,300 babies born with birth defects because of Accutane. Some of the babies were so deformed that they died in pain after only a few years of life in an institution. Probably many times more babies had mild cognitive defects. And what is worse, despite all efforts, rates of birth defects never went down until iPLEDGE.

No one deserves that, for any reason.

Doug Bremner, M.D., is author of *Before You Take That Pill*.

[Update] *The New York Times* has still not written an article about the health risks of Accutane. In fact, a few months back I was interviewed by a journalism student who was writing her thesis on why Accutane was never covered by *The New York Times* or other major media. The only major article was done by Kevin McCoy in *USA Today*.[10] A documentary was made in 2008 called *Morire per la pelle* (Skin to Die For) which was only available in Italian until I put English and

French subtitles on it and posted it on my <u>YouTube channel</u> this year (jamesdouglasbremner).[11]

Chapter 8: The Ups and Downs of the Stock Market: A Personal Perspective

Why not interpret the stock market from the point of view of my personal life? Yes, me. Doug Bremner. I mean why not? Maybe the events of my life have an influence on the stock market.

By <u>Doug Bremner, Contributor</u>

(Originally posted October 31, 2008, in *The Huffington Post*).

We've known for some time that no one can predict the stock market, and that the efforts of stock pickers routinely come out worse than chance. Now we are learning that no one has a clue about what to do about the current financial meltdown, or where the Dow Jones Industrial Average (DJIA) will go in the future.

So, I thought I would try a new approach. Why not interpret the stock market from the point of view of my personal life? Yes, me. Doug Bremner. I mean why not? Maybe the events of my life and those of my family have an influence on the stock market. Or something like that.

So, let's look at the data. When my mother was born on February 23, 1932 (a most fortuitous event for me, personally), the DJIA closed at 62. As you can see from the graph, her birth in 1932, helped pull us out of the stock market crash of 1929 and its aftermath, the Great Depression.

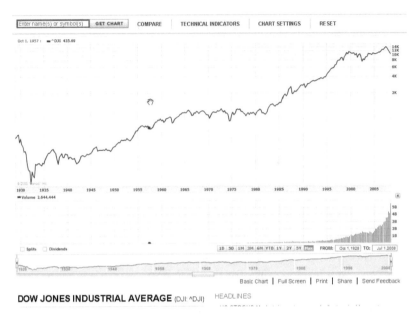

DOW JONES INDUSTRIAL AVERAGE (DJI: ^DJI)   HEADLINES

No wonder my dad always said to put all your money in the stock market!

From the date of her birth, through her childhood until the birth of her first child, my brother Steve, in 1955, surely seen as a positive event by her and my brother, at least, the DJIA climbed upward to 410, a six-fold increase.

Not bad! From 1955 to February 12, 1966, the untimely day my mother died at the age of 33 (yes, sad, I know) the stock market rose from 410 to 989, a more than two-fold increase.

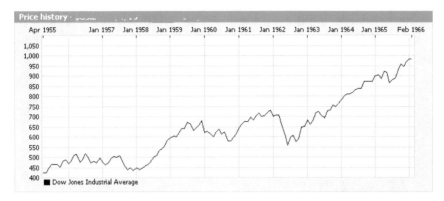

When the stock market opened the next Monday, it dropped by -1%, of course. Here is a picture of me just before my mother died, at the age of 4 1/2. I use it for my Facebook page.

My wife uses that as evidence that I am "stuck" at that period of my life. From my perspective I put it up there just because... I can. After being made fun of as a child for always saying "when I was about four..." I am saying "when I was about four" with a vengeance.

The book, btw, is "Father's Dragon." I can't tell you if it was a good book or not, I don't remember. I do remember thinking that the book should be part of our family portrait, though. My mom liked to read too. Here she is as a child in Almira, WA.

I'm not sure what the name of her book was though. Oh, back to the stock market. After my mother died, the stock market and I stagnated throughout my childhood, going from 989 in 1966 to 888 in June of 1979, when I graduated from high school.

Coincidence? After graduation, things went better for me, with a string of successes including graduation from college, medical school at Duke, residency at Yale, launching of my career and success in romance culminating in marriage to my lovely wife Viola in

Taormina, Italy on August 1, 1990, during which the Dow zoomed from 888 to 2905, a three-fold increase.

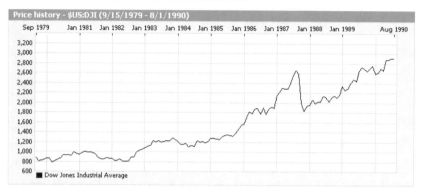

Yippee! And we're still married!

As the little ones started to tumble out of my wife's belly it was a good thing that we put our money for our retirement and their educational futures entirely into the stock market as stocks continued to go up until December of 2007 when the Dow closed at 13,264, a five-fold increase!

Why did I pick December of 2007? That was when Roche Pharmaceuticals attacked me for daring to insist that their blockbuster drug for acne, Accutane, that surely caused teens to smile, could actually make some teens depressed? After that the Dow has dropped almost 3,000 points, closing September 29, 2008, at 10,371.

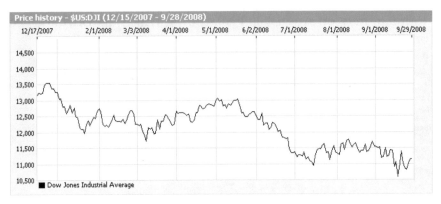

Price history - $US:DJI (12/15/2007 - 9/28/2008)

So, the moral of the story? Live right and the rest will follow (?). Karma drives the Dow? Or that the bad Karma of corporations are driving our country into the ground? Literally?

By the way, we're having a memorial party for my mom this weekend, so I recommend... buy!

Update, June 5, 2014: What doesn't break you, right? Well, I survived the attentions of Roche, and my career's continued to thrive. Roche hasn't had such good times. Last year their lawyers got in trouble for asking Accutane victims whether or not they had anal sex, and how often they went to mass. And in 2011, with lawsuits piling up, Roche took Accutane off the market! Yeah!

And guess what? The stock market has been doing pretty since back in 2008. Yesterday the Dow closed at 16,821. And me and Mrs. Bremner have continued to put all of our 401K money into stocks, so it looks like we're headed to a pretty good retirement!

The only problem is that since I checked in on the ups and downs of the stock market back in 2008, the U.S. Supreme Court has declared corporations to be people. So now that Roche is a person, I'm afraid he's going to come and kill me.

Maybe with all the money I got from the stock market, I can hire a bodyguard. Lol.

[Update] We've done pretty well since I wrote this. Still married, got a farm in Italy, and our stock portfolio has done well too. The whole

Roche thing kind of through me off track for a while in terms of my academic career. At one point I wrote and directed an independent feature length comedy film called *Inheritance, Italian Style* (71% on Rotten Tomatoes, yes!). That was sort of a response like, screw you, guys, I'm gonna go do something else. But I still am trying to produce my next film based on a screenplay I wrote, *The Goose That Laid the Golden Egg*. When my research grant funding ran out, however, I realized I had to get my shit together, and now I am pretty much back on track in the research and academic thing. Oh, and Roche had to pay me for all that time I spent in depositions with them, so I was able to pay off my medical school loans (finally) and get on a better financial track. Here's a view from our farm-house in Southern Tuscany:

Chapter 9: Update on Physician Corruption by Pharma

(Originally posted November 5, 2008, in *Drug Safety and Health News*).

In today's issue of *JAMA* there is a <u>letter to the editor</u> by Ross et al describing the results of a study of payments to physicians by drug companies in the State of Vermont, which has a law requiring disclosure of these payments.[12] Physicians got a total of 21,409 payments in a two year period totaling $4.9 million, 56% of which was designated "trade secrets." The authors were able to obtain details of these so called "trade secret" payments only through litigation and extensive efforts. However, the "trade secret" information turned out to be payments for talks, education, and dinners.

Hands in the cookie jar

How do those things count as trade secrets?

Why are they trying to keep these payments a secret?

Why can't physicians just pay for their own talks anyway?

[Update: The Physicians Payments Sunshine Act (Sunshine Act), part of the Affordable Care Act (ACA), came about as a result of negative publicity about pharmaceutical company payments to physicians. The Sunshine Act was introduced to the Senate by Senator Charles Grassley of Iowa and driven largely by his aid, Paul Thacker, and passed in 2010. The Sunshine Act requires manufacturers of drugs, medical devices, and biologicals that participate in U.S. federal health care programs to report payments and items of value of over $10 given to physicians and teaching hospitals. It has led to a major change in the relationship between academic physicians and industry since the time of the writing of this original post.]

Chapter 10: Abilify Me to Help Me Find the Usefulness of This Drug for Depression

(Originally posted November 6, 2008, in *Drug Safety & Health News*).

Bristol Myers Squibb (BMS) recently started a TV ad for their drug Abilify (aripiprazole) which has gotten a lot of people in a tizzy prompting me to look closer at this new claim for a psychiatric drug. First of all, I previously gave honorable mention to Abilify as one of the medications with the goofiest names "Where Do They Come Up with those Goofy Names for Prescription Medications Anyway?")

Abilify Me Please

Back then I mused that perhaps the manufacturers thought that their anti-psychotic pill would make non-functional mental patients jump out of their chairs and start climbing the corporate ladder. Well, I don't know if it will make you climb the corporate ladder, but the akathisia you could get might make you feel like you wanted to jump out of a chair. Not to mention wanting to jump up and go pee if you develop second generation antipsychotic-induced diabetes. This medication is an antipsychotic (apparently not mentioned in the TV ads) and these drugs can have some nasty side effects.

So, is this drug really useful for depression? The ads hype the fact that over half of people may not respond to antidepressant medications, but that seems like a self-serving turnaround on the part of the drug companies (including BMS maker of Serzone (nefazodone)) who have been telling us for years that their antidepressant drugs are magic bullets for depression.

So, what do the studies actually show?

In the first study of Abilify, 362 patients were randomly assigned to Abilify or placebo for six weeks after a failed trial of antidepressants. There was a -8.8 v -5.8 change on the Montgomery Asberg Depression Rating Scale (MADRS), a difference of 11.5%. 23% of patients on Abilify versus 5% on placebo had akathisia, a potentially very disturbing side effect where you feel like you are jumping out of your skin or cannot sit still. Restlessness was seen in 14% v 3%. Fatigue was also more common.[13]

In the second study of Abilify, 381 patients who had failed at least one antidepressant medication trial were treated for eight weeks with an antidepressant followed by the addition of Abilify or a placebo for six weeks. Abilify showed an -8.5 change on the 26 item Montgomery Asberg Depression Rating Scale (MADRS) versus -5.7 for placebo, a difference of 2.8 points, a difference of 11%. 26% of patients on Abilify versus 4% on placebo had akathisia, and 10% versus 1% had restlessness.[14]

Conclusions? Abilify is more likely to make you want to jump out of your skin than it is to cure your depression. An 11% improvement over placebo is not that great and is set off by the fact that Abilify has a lot of nasty side effects and doesn't work better than other treatments of refractory depression like lithium (which also can have nasty side effects). I don't watch TV ads because I have TiVo, but I can only imagine how it was presented by BMS.

That settled, now we can move on to my favorite study that I found in the literature: Egashira N et al, Aripiprazole inhibits marble-burying behavior via 5-hydroxytryptamine (5-HT)1A receptor-independent mechanisms. *European Journal of Pharmacology*. 592(1-3):103-8, 2008 Sep 11.

Searching for my marbles

I wonder if the September 11 publication date is a coincidence? OK, conspiracy theory time now. Maybe BMS is trying to tell us that if our government officials had been on Abilify they wouldn't have lost their marbles and allowed 9/11 to become a reality?

Any other theories?

[disclosures: In addition to consulting to competing drug companies listed in my "disclosures" link I have also co-authored papers both with some of the authors of the Abilify studies as well as physicians who have given CME activities that endorsed the use of Abilify for the treatment of depression.]

Anonymous Reader wrote on November 7, 2008

Doug,

I think you've gone too far this time. For years, I've been trying to find a way to stop my mice from burying their marbles without affecting their locomotor activity, and now we finally have an effective agent, thanks to the creative geniuses at Kyushu University and Otsuka Pharmaceuticals. At least our taxpayer money didn't go into this one!

Doug Bremner wrote on November 7, 2008

Anonymous, just writing in jest. I have nothing against research on marbles, just thought the study title sounded funny. Cheers.

Therapy Patient wrote on November 12, 2008

I couldn't link to the marble-burying article because it required a password, but if marble-burying represents anxiety (in a lab animal?) then I'd agree (though I enjoyed your humorous interpretation more). My interpretation of what I feel when I take Abilify (1 pill of 5mg dose after not having been on the medication for many months) is a dramatic reduction in anxiety in 20-30 minutes, so I imagine if I buried marbles when anxious that I'd stop.

Not counting the many things, I experienced which were possible side-effects, the effect I disliked the most about Abilify was the way it took away my feelings. Gone. I did not feel happy or sad. I lost my sense of humor and effectively became a robot. I typically am not depressed though, so am not in the same situation as the study subjects. A positive effect was that oddly, I lost all tendencies to procrastinate, focused on the most important thing first and got large quantities of work done. It's not a fair trade off for me, though.

Doug Bremner wrote on November 12, 2008

Welcome, therapy patient. I have no idea what marble burying is supposed to represent. I just thought it sounded funny. Personally, I lost my marbles years ago and haven't been able to find them since.

[Update: I do a lot more clinical psychiatry now in 2023 than I did in 2008 and I do prescribe Abilify to some patients with severe depression. Most of these studies showing marginal benefit were in patients with mild or moderate depression. For patients with severe depression the benefit is more pronounced.]

Now read online, "Is Chromium Useful for the Treatment of Diabetes?"[15]

Chapter 11: Our President's [Secret] Parting Gift to Corporations: A Get Out of Jail Free Card

(Originally posted November 7, 2008, in *Drug Safety & Health News*).

President George Bush's lasting legacy may very well be a revamping of the judicial system. Our country is based on a balance of the judicial, executive, and legislative branches of the government, and an appropriate balance between the power of the states and the federal government. However, in a bizarre subversion of the supposed aims of the Republican party to diminish the role of the federal government in everyday lives, the Bush administration over the past eight years has carried on a secret campaign to take away individual liberties and build a Big Brother type of government which controls everything. This includes things like the Patriot Act, but more subtly in a pay-back to the corporations that got him elected, he has worked to give corporations a get out of jail free card in the form of immunity from prosecution.

Here's your get-out-of-jail free card.

As described in a recent report prepared by the <u>American Association for Justice</u>, based on Freedom of Information Act requests for correspondence within multiple US agencies that regulate everything from prescription medications to automobiles, there has been a systematic effort to insert language into the rules written by these regulatory bodies to remove corporations from liability for the products that these federal agencies cover. The report states:

> *This language would effectively block all product*
> *liability lawsuits from being adjudicated and would let*
> *corporations "get-out-of-jail-free" even when their*
> *products seriously injure or even kill Americans.*

I have been primarily interested in how this plays out in the field of prescription medications, where the FDA has been pushing the concept of preemption, which means that citizens can't sue a drug company in state courts if a drug has been approved by the FDA, since the federal government "preempts" state law (see "No Redemption for Preemption").

This concept is a misinterpretation of the law and represents an attempt to eviscerate one of the three branches of our government, the judicial. Considering how the executive branch has ignored the legislative branch (not responding to subpoenas, etc.) I guess they would prefer a fascist-style dictatorship. And you may think you don't have to worry because of the recent election results but the placement of like-minded individuals in the judicial branch from the Supreme Court on down is a lasting legacy that we will have to deal with for years to come. The current case of Wyeth v Levine before the Supreme Court will represent the first ruling on preemption related to prescription drugs.

Emails contained in the report document how agencies within the federal government have corresponded with one another to promote this concept. To give one example, Dan Troy, ex chief counsel for the FDA, had bona fide credentials as member of the American Enterprise Institute and other conservative organizations, and made over $100,000 per year consulting to the drug maker Pfizer. He was given his pick of where to go in the new Bush administration and chose to go to the FDA where he was effectively the leader since there was no permanent Director. As documented in the AAJ report, in the two-year period he was there he met 129 times with representatives of the pharmaceutical industry [his predecessor met with them once] before he eventually resigned under a growing cloud related to his promotion of pharma.[16] While at the FDA he told representatives of pharma that they should "give a Hollywood pitch" to the FDA to get them to file friends of the court briefs on behalf of drug companies being sued for toxic side effects of their drugs under the rationale that if the FDA approved it, they had an interest in seeing that no liability was found.

Troy eventually concluded that filing all those briefs took too much time, so he came up with the language of preemption, and the administration worked to stack the courts in favor of this bogus idea, and the rest is history (e.g., Wyeth v Levine).

It will probably take legislation to undo this crime, which is if the legislative branch still exists.

Henry Greenspan wrote on November 7, 2008

I like your piece about the history of preemption. I would just add two points.

First, the move from "script-pitching" to full preemption was not simply a development of the past six years. Even before Dan Troy was at FDA, the strategy was set. It is a classic case of "regulatory take-over" of which there is a long history. Fight a regulatory agency for years (as Dan Troy did as a lawyer for big tobacco and pharma); become the effective head of it; gut it; and then canonize (via preemption) what's left. As you note, this pattern goes far beyond FDA.

Relatedly, it is important to underline that preemption is the heir to radical de-regulation. The logic is explained in the notion of regulatory take-over above. Thus, the current preemption movement has deep roots (and funding sources) that 'blossomed' as public policy with Reagan, but really goes back quite a bit earlier. Once again, the logic is: Take-over the hen house; deconstruct it; and then declare it omniscient.

Henry Greenspan, Ph.D.

University of Michigan

Doug Bremner wrote on November 7, 2008

I guess that is how the fascists got their start.

Viola Vaccarino wrote on November 7, 2008

If we say that drug companies, once they get their products approved by FDA, are no longer liable for side effects, then doctors, once they get board certified, are no longer liable for medical errors. Does this make sense?

Mary wrote on November 7, 2008

Look at what is happening in China--melamine in baby food, lead in toys, etc. We count on our ability to bring companies to their knees with lawsuits to protect ourselves from those situations...without that, greed prevails.

Matthew Holford wrote on November 7, 2008

URL: http://itsquiteanexperience.blogspot.com/

Comment: Simple solution: don't buy the f***ing products.

Marcia wrote on November 7, 2008

How did Wyeth v. Levine become a product liability case? My understanding was the patient's arm had to be amputated because the drug was accidentally administered IA push, and was settled for malpractice? I've read a couple of summaries of the case, but…

Doug Bremner wrote on November 7, 2008

Because Levine said that Wyeth should have stated on the package that an i.v. should be started (would have prevented this event).

[Update: What can I say, things have only gotten worse. Now we have corporations viewed by the Supreme Court as "persons." Yikes! And we have to have our babies now. Oh, and speaking of Hollywood Pitches, I have more experience with that than your average blogging psychiatrist. So don't forget to watch my movie, "Inheritance, Italian Style," on amazon, tubi, plex, etc., etc. We're fund-raising now to make The Goose That Laid the Golden Egg into a movie as well.

]

Chapter 12: Dear Doctor: Cipro, Avelox, and Levaquin Can Make Your Tendons Snap Off

(Originally posted November 8, 2008, in *Drug News & Health Safety Blog*).

That's a translation into person speak from a letter I got today from Bayer Healthcare Pharmaceuticals that started out with "Dear Healthcare Professional" and went on to their new "black box warning" for their antibiotic drugs Avelox (moxifloxacin hydrochloride) and Cipro (ciprofloxacin). Here is their warning:

> *Fluoroquinolones, including Avelox/Cipro, are associated with an increased risk of tendinitis and tendon rupture in all ages. This risk is further increased in older patients usually over 60 years of age, in patients taking corticosteroid drugs, and in patients with kidney, heart or lung transplants.*

Well, it's about time. I wrote about this nasty habit of Cipro to snap tendons and mess up joints over a year ago in my book[17] because at the time Cipro was the most poorly rated drug on askapatient.com. I hate to say I told you so, but I did tell you so. It's just too bad that it took the manufacturers a couple of years to get the word out. I wish people in the healthcare industry would read these websites, which patients go to only out of desperation.

Unfortunately, 81% of the time this toxic drug, Cipro, is prescribed inappropriately,[18] and 32% of women get this drug inappropriately for new onset urinary tract infections, when the preferred first drug is Septra.

Another drug in the same class as Cipro is Levaquin (levofloxacin), which is the third most discussed drug on medications.com, just behind my other two faves, Yasmin (the birth control pill that might make you nuts) and Singulair (montelukast, an asthma drug with similar problems). Levaquin and like drugs also seem to drive people nuts, which reinforces my conclusion that when it comes to drug companies, if they don't kill you, they might drive you crazy.

So let's all sing "I need a drug that won't drive me crazy" to the tune of "I need a lover that won't drive me crazy," by John Cougar Mellencamp.

[Update: In addition to Accutane, I have been contacted numerous times by patients and their families suffering from neuropsychiatric side effects from Singular and Levaquin (in addition to the other fluoroquinolones), which could be mediated by effects on mitochondria. Since this original post it has become increasingly clear that fluoroquinolones are overutilized. A number of reports have come out since this original post highlighting the fact that fluoroquinolones impair mitochondrial function,[19] have effects on motor function and induce anxiety and depression like behavior in mice, and cause an increase in psychiatric side effects[20] including depression and anxiety. After reading my original post, I was contacted by Dr Beatrice A. Golomb of the University of California, San Diego, who was the author of this paper[21] on the psychiatric and cartilage effects of the fluoroquinolones. She is currently recruiting for another study on side effects of these drugs. Linda Martin, Ph.D., provided me with a table showing 602 and upward of 6,020 suicides and suicidal behaviors in patients on fluoroquinolones reported to the FDA Adverse Events Reporting System (FAERS) from 2007-2015.

Total Levaquin, Cipro, and Avelox FDA Adverse Events Reporting System (FAERS) Data November 01, 1997 – July 28, 2015	Actual Suicide-Related Adverse Events Reported to FAERS	The FDA Assumes Only 10% of Adverse Events are Reported to the FDA; Estimated Actual Adverse Events
Suicide		
Suicidal ideation	348	3,480
Completed suicide	133	1,330
Suicide attempt	76	760
Self injurious behavior	18	180
Self injurious ideation	15	150
Suicidal behaviour	11	110
Intentional self-injury	1	10
Total	602	6,020

Now read online, "Quinolone Antibiotics Can Have Some Nasty Side Effects."[22]

Chapter 13: Jupiter is Not Likely to Turn On Aphrodite

(Originally posted November 10, 2008, in *Drug Safety & Health News*).

Mrs. Bremner [DOCTOR BREMNER to YOU guys!] is attending the Annual Meeting of the American Heart Association this week in New Orleans and texted me some news about the release today of results from the JUPITeR study ("Justification for the Use of statins in Prevention: an Intervention Trial evaluating Rosuvastatin (JUPITeR)") published in the New England Journal of Medicine.[23]

Jupiter

(gasp), Oh really. I think this one would definitely not have been a turn on for Aphrodite.

Ha, ha.

Based on the results of this study, that a biomarker of heart disease, C-reactive Protein (CRP), predicts response to the drug Crestor (rosuvastatin) (and not just total cholesterol or LDL cholesterol), the authors of this study would apparently like us to come to the conclusion that, basically, all of us should be on a statin medication for the prevention of heart disease. In fact, I can already hear the shills and the media saying "revolutionary" and "likely to change practice"! In fact, there is even a cheesy site on the New England's website asking us how it will change our practices (gasp, shame).

We've been through this drill before, when our country's "leading" cardiologists informed us that statins were so great that they should be put in the drinking water.

But now, let us turn our attention to the results of the JUPITeR trial.

17,802 healthy men and women with LDL cholesterol of less than 130 mg per deciliter and CRPs of greater than 2.0 mg per liter were given either rosuvastatin 20 mg per day or placebo. They were then followed for the occurrence of the "combined primary endpoint" of heart attack, stroked, arterial revascularization, hospitalization for unstable angina, or death from cardiovascular causes.

First of all, whenever doctors start combining real disease outcomes (like dying of a heart attack) with what are primarily... er... inconveniences, like going to the hospital, you have to start wondering about the study.

OK. So, what about the results, you say. For their primary outcome out of 100 people treated each year there were 0.77 versus 1.36 who had an event like heart attack, hospitalization, etc. That is a difference of 0.59%. But I am going to ignore their cheesy primary endpoint and look at what to me matters, which is heart attacks. For each year of treatment out of 100 people 0.17 in the Crestor group versus 0.37 in the placebo group had a heart attack, or a difference of 0.2%, which would have amounted to a 1% difference over five years if the study had continued for that long, but the study committee cheerfully "stopped" the study after 1.9 years since they thought things were going so well that it would be "unethical" to continue the study (Hooray!).

I guess that 1% of responders outweighs the 3% or so that will develop liver toxicity or muscle damage.

Study results that will change clinical practice, indeed.

BTW, look at the end of the article for the long list of consulting agreements to the pharmaceutical industry engaged in by the authors of the study. And funding by AstraZeneca.

COMMENTS

Viola Vaccarino wrote on November 10, 2008

The study excluded subjects with diabetes or hypertension and there was a four week "placebo" run in phase and subjects who were not compliant during that phase were dropped. 80% of the patients were excluded and many more were excluded during the placebo run in phase. What this means for the regular patient is unknown.

Marilyn Mann wrote on November 10, 2008

Just read this. Wondering why you did not mention 20% reduction in total mortality. Also, interesting that women benefited to the same extent as men.

See studies published ahead-of-print yesterday in Circulation and Circulation Cardiovascular Quality and Outcomes for more info on CRP.

C-Reactive Protein and Parental History Improve Global Cardiovascular Risk Prediction. The Reynolds Risk Score for Men Paul M Ridker, Nina P. Paynter, Nader Rifai, J. Michael Gaziano, and Nancy R. Cook Circulation published 9 November 2008, 10.1161/CIRCULATIONAHA.108.814251

C-Reactive Protein and Reclassification of Cardiovascular Risk in the Framingham Heart Study Peter W.F. Wilson, Michael Pencina, Paul Jacques, Jacob Selhub, Ralph D'Agostino, and Christopher J. O'Donnell Circ Cardiovasc Qual Outcomes published 9 November 2008, 10.1161/CIRCOUTCOMES.108.831198

Doug Bremner wrote on November 10, 2008

The reduction in total mortality was 1.0 per 100 patient years versus 1.25 in the placebo group, a difference of 25% in relative risk, but of 0.25% in absolute risk (i.e., not that great). I think one thing this study highlights are that maybe LDL reduction is not the "cause" of risk reduction, or at least exclusively.

The other issue is what the clinical implications of this study are. Are doctors going to check CRP and LDL in everyone and treat whoever fits either profile? That means everyone will be on this stuff. Crazy.

David Diamond wrote on November 10, 2008

Doug – great commentary on the Jupiter trial and kudos to you for your muckraking blog. The whole statin revolution seems driven by big pharma greed with little real benefit to the population, followed by sheep-like docs who can't see the flaws in the research. Can you imagine turning the CHD word upside down by showing better CHD outcomes with a diet low in sugar and high in chocolate vs a statin?

Odysseas wrote on November 10, 2008

Again, I think people get so enamored by the relative risk that they don't even consider the difference in absolute risk or the Number Needed to Treat (NNT)... (The calculation may be useful for some readers) As the fanfare dies down, perhaps a thoughtful discussion will ensue...

Doug Bremner wrote on November 10, 2008

Yes, the relative risk v absolute risk distinction is critical. The story I use is for primary prevention in men with risk factors. Out of 100 men, 4 men on placebo will have a heart attack in five years v 3 on a statin. If you told someone that a drug would reduce his risk of having a heart attack by 25% (and told him none of the risks, he would take it! If you went into a room of 100 men and said I want you all to take a drug and it will prevent only one of you from having a heart attack, but three of you will have some liver damage or muscle pain, and maybe it causes cancer but we are not sure, they wouldn't take it. Both describe the same situation (going from 3 to 4 is a 25% change (relative risk) but 4%-3%=1%). Crucial distinction. Most doctors don't understand, but the pharma detail people do. And they always use the one that suits them best. Also, NNT is the number needed to treat. Means that (in this case) 31 patients need to be treated for four years to save one from a cardiovascular event or procedure (their primary outcome). Which isn't all that great. The authors pointed out that this is similar to prior studies of those with high LDL, but all that says is that LDL is not the be all and end all (the cardiology research community has been moving toward the inflammatory pathways area for several years now; elevated CRP is probably associated with the metabolic syndrome, etc.).

Chapter 14: Will You Be My Friend?

(Originally posted November 11, 2008, in *Drug Safety & Health News*).

OK, enough of gods, goddesses, cardiologists, and the beings that they impregnate. Those cardiologists will never listen to me any way. Soon everyone over 50 will be on a statin! Anyway, back to the humble world of emotion, psychiatry, and the question of...

...will you be my friend?

That's right, folks, facebook time. And blogging. Front and center.

I had a story about the 'will you be my friend' quote but it isn't appropriate for public consumption.

Anyhoo, you know what I am talking about. Using your mouse to point your cursor at someone's name on Facebook and then waiting for their response, and then...

...voila! You have a new friend!

[heart goes pitter patter, etc.]

I have become 'friends' with people I have never met, who 'friended' me because they read my book, and then 'introduced' me to others who had written books on similar topics, or had similar views, or were liberals like me, and I became 'friends' to them sight unseen. I found the exchange all quite exhilarating, liking being at a fancy ball. It didn't matter much to me that I had never met them. I just liked reading their posts, causes, and status updates. And for old college friends and the like the where are you now stuff is kind of interesting.

My fellow shrinks blogging on ShrinkRap have written about the psychological meaning of facebook.

I agree with them that you should not "friend" your patient, your doctor, your children or your parents. You can, however, friend nieces and nephews, siblings, spouses, old schoolmates, and (disagreeing with them, I feel that if you want you can friend) people you have never met but who share similar interests.

As I wrote on their site, facebook is a way for vapid narcissists (such as myself) to form weak relationships with others through the internet. In my "book" it is fine to friend people you don't know who share a similar interest, in my case health and drug news.

However, I have attempted to 'friend' others who had similar interests, who responded:

> *Hi Doug, have we actually ever met?*

To which I had to reply in the negative, although I said I had read his writing, and sent him a link to my blog, which he never responded to, which left me with a feeling of...

sadness... [head down, sniff] ... emptiness (especially since Mrs. Bremner is away at the AHA this week)

Which leads me to the next topic, being 'out there' on the internet.

A friend of mine was sending some of my post to a yahoo group and so I joined, not knowing anything about these groups. And then when I quoted some of the things they were saying someone said they felt 'violated' because these comments were not for public discussion. She informed me that the 'rules' were that comments in the 'group' were private.

I realized I really knew nothing of these 'groups' or whether the comments were public or private. I needed Emily Post for the internet.

Here is another example. In my initial enthusiasm for my blog when I got copied on emails for health-related things, I would put people on my email list. I posted that they should say 'unsubscribe' if they wanted off. But I have since learned that some people think that is a violation to have to say 'unsubscribe'. So, I no longer put people on my list unless they ask. Now I have figured out RSS feed (say Dinosaur, duh!) people can choose for themselves.

And if you want to get off of this list, say *unsubscribe* or f**k off!

Or, if you don't take me off of this list, I will blog about you! (Real comment)

Ciao.

COMMENTS

Rickey wrote on November 11, 2008

Great blog as always Doug!

Dan wrote on November 11, 2008

Check out the Wikipedia link for facebook.

With the advent of social networking, an irony is occurring. On some such site, one may share intimate details about themselves, and their lives yet have not spoken with their neighbor across the street since last year. It is because we are bombarded with [information from the internet]

Dinah wrote on November 11, 2008

Greetings from the Shrink Rappers!

Doug Bremner wrote on November 11, 2008

Dinah on the web site Shrink Rap pointed out her post on psychiatrists as bloggers here.

And I got the quote of the day there based on my comment that psychiatrists are not magicians or mind readers and cannot be blamed for all the adverse reactions our patients have to psychiatric drugs which led to a lively ongoing discussion on that site.

btw the person I blogged about agreed to be my friend! [not sure if he read my post first though]

[Update] On the subject of being "friends" that I hinted I could not comment on at the time, now that the field of psychiatry has gone bonzo over the use of hallucinogenic drugs for the treatment of psychiatric disorders or as an adjunct to psychotherapy, I can speak about my experiences in this realm with more freedom. I write about my first experience with hallucinogenic mushrooms in my narrative non-fiction book *The Goose That Laid the Golden Egg*. My second experience involved connecting with a friend from college and his new list of friends. After taking hallucinogenic mushrooms I went up to each of them and asked, "Are you my friend?" The experience did not go well. As for facebook, I am now friends with my children. Aren't we all?

Chapter 15: Remind Me Why I Should Be on Plavix?

(Originally posted November 12, 2008, in *Drug Safety & Health News*).

A study of 16,690-persons whose results were released today by Medco Health Solutions found that patients taking Plavix (clopidogrel) with a proton pump inhibitor (PPI) like Nexium (esomeprazole) or Prilosec (omeprazole) have a 50% increase in risk of major cardiovascular event and 74% increase in heart attacks compared to people taking Plavix alone. Since Plavix is given to prevent heart attacks as an expensive alternative to aspirin, it seems these people are losing their benefit.

Where does that leave us? Well since about half of Plavix users are on Nexium or another PPI to prevent stomach bleeding, we have to ask what is the benefit of Plavix for these people? So, what has the data been for Plavix in the prevention of cardiovascular events up to now.

In the CAPRIE study Plavix treated patients showed an 5.32% annual rate of a composite measure of stroke, heart attack, or vascular death, compared with 5.83% on aspirin treated patients, a difference that was barely statistically significant.[24] In the CHARISMA trial of patients with heart disease or risk factors for heart disease there was no significant difference between those who were given clopidogrel plus aspirin or aspirin alone in the combined incidence of heart attack, stroke, or death from cardiovascular causes.[25] In the CLOpidogrel and Metoprolol Infarction Trial (COMMIT) 45,852 patients with a heart attack within the past 24 hours were given clopidogrel or placebo in addition to aspirin. Clopidogrel patients had a 9% reduction in a combined measure of death, heart attack or stroke, a difference that was statistically significant.[26] An analysis of all of the published studies showed a 10% reduction in heart attacks and strokes in patients with a history of cardiovascular disease when clopidogrel was added to aspirin.[27] These differences, however, translate into a less than 1% reduction in absolute risk. In the Management of ATherothrombosis with Clopidogrel in High-risk patients (MATCH) study, 7,599 patients with recent stroke or TIA with one other risk factor for heart disease were randomly assigned to receive clopidogrel or clopidogrel plus aspirin.[28] There was no difference in rates of combined stroke, heart attack, or hospitalization between clopidogrel (17%) and clopidogrel plus aspirin (16%); a 1.3% increase in bleeding was not statistically significant. In a study of 320 patients who had developed a bleeding ulcer while taking aspirin to prevent heart disease, after the patients' ulcers healed, they were randomized for a year to re-treatment with aspirin or clopidogrel. All of them also received esomeprazole. The patients who took clopidogrel had more gastrointestinal bleeding (8.6%) than aspirin patients (0.7%), a difference that is striking.[29]

It looks like with these new study results whatever meagre advantage Plavix has over aspirin are more than offset in people on Nexium as well. It is hard to see what role Plavix has now in heart attack prevention relative to the cheaper aspirin.

[30]Now read online, "Do I Have An Ulcer or Is It Just Gastroesophageal Reflux Disease (GERD)?"

Chapter 16: First, They're Drugging Our Drinking Water, Now Our Kids, What Next?

(Originally posted November 19, 2008, in *Drug Safety & Health News*).

It's bad enough that they are drugging our drinking water but now I guess they are afraid that our kids are going to be drinking out of mud puddles instead of the faucet or toilet so now they are giving their drugs directly to our kids in the form of a prescription. An article in *The New York Times* today by Gardiner Harris described the findings of an FDA outside expert advisory panel that concluded that antipsychotic (or neuroleptic) medications are being given too often to children.[31] 389,000 children were treated last year with Risperdal (risperidone) alone, many of them for ADHD. This is in spite of the fact that neuroleptic medications like Risperdal (risperidone) and Zyprexa (olanzapine) are not approved for the treatment of Attention Deficit Hyperactivity Disorder (ADHD). The use of these drugs has increased five-fold in the past decade and a half.

We also have the specter of two-year-olds being diagnosed with bipolar disorder and treated with these medications. Well, I have already given you my opinion about the diagnosis of bi-polar disorder.

Oh don't look so surprised -- I told you before that I was "Bi-Polar."

"Oh, don't look so surprised. I told you I was bi-polar."

The committee said they were "frustrated" and that a stronger label warning was needed because of the risks of diabetes, obesity, and tardive dyskinesia. But the FDA basically shrugged their shoulders and said that the problem lies with the prescribing doctors and that the medical societies need to do more education. I would have to agree with other writers on the topic that a medical culture of overuse of these medications and underemphasis of risk is largely to blame for the problem.

OK, here's your education:

Stop giving antipsychotics to kids who don't have the diagnosis of childhood schizophrenia.

Chapter 17: The Infinite Reach of the Pharmaceutical Industry: Have a Prozac with your Cheeseburger

(Originally posted November 21, 2008, in *Drug Safety & Health News*).

A quote from a physician describing the results of a study published this week in the *New Well*, it is not enough that pharma has spread its influence through the medical industrial complex, it looks like they also have infiltrated the medical media as well. The psychiatrist host of the National Public Radio show "The Infinite Mind", which deals with psychiatry and brain related topics, Fred Goodwin, M.D., was found to have taken more than $1.2 million in speaking fees from Glaxo since 2000 which was not disclosed on the show or to the producers of the show, in violation of NPR's policies.[32] Some of the shows came out in support of the diagnosis of childhood bipolar disorder and against the idea that SSRI antidepressant medications can make you suicidal, showing evidence of bias in favor of pharma that is not consistent with the actual evidence. He also had as a guest on the show Peter Pitts who was introduced as a "Former FDA Commissioner" when in fact he was at the time working for a PR firm that had pharma companies as their clients, a fact that was not disclosed. Topic? SSRI antidepressants are safe and effective and cannot make you have suicidal thoughts. [Not true, read the literature guys].

It makes you wonder, though. Why would anyone think that people wouldn't figure out that they were getting income from pharma when they are jetting all around the country giving talks? And didn't the psychiatrists listening to the talks wonder who was paying for all this?

Duh!

It really is sad, but I guess we shouldn't expect much from a news service that was little more than a couple of people sitting around commenting on the news collected by others until the heiress of the

McDonald's cheeseburger chain, Joan Kroc, dumped $200 million of her wealth onto NPR in one big fat donation.

McDonald's cheeseburger

It is a little-known fact that that donation allowed them to mushroom (or should I say balloon?) with new bureaus at multiple sites throughout the world. However, to retain their image as the "people's news" they continued to have those stupid fundraising telethons where you have to listen to the mournful voice of the *This American Life* guy laying a guilt trip on us about donating. And you never hear them yacking about the pile they got from the cheeseburger queen. I guess maybe they feel a little guilty about that. We used to hear them give little announcements from Kaiser Permanente about how blueberries might prevent Alzheimer's Disease, so eat some blueberries. I wrote a blog about that making fun of them after which they stopped, although I don't know if they were one of the ten readers of my blog at that time, so I am not sure if it was in response to my scathing criticism of their idiotic public "health" service announcements.

I have some other public health service announcement suggestions they could use. How about, why don't you use a medicated stent for your coronary artery disease (CAD) so that you can be more likely to have a coronary artery clot off? Or why don't you take some Nexium with your Plavix so that you can increase your risk of heart attack? Or why don't you go cold turkey on your Paxil so you can become acutely suicidal? Or why don't you take Abilify so that you can feel like jumping out of your skin? Or why don't you take some Accutane for that zit so you can become depressed? Or take some Chantix (varenicline) to stop smoking, which can make you suicidal, so that you can stop wondering about whether or not your life will be cut prematurely short by cancer.

I could, of course, go on and on.

I personally would give more to NPR if they stopped sending me letters addressed to my first name with my wife's last name. How... de-testosterone-izing [I couldn't think of a good word, so I had to make one up].

Here's some health news you won't hear on NPR. People who eat in fast food restaurants like McDonald's three or more times a week have a greater than 90% chance of developing heart disease or diabetes. The increase in diabetes world-wide can be directly linked to the spread of McDonald's and similar fast-food restaurants throughout the world (see later in the volume, "A Growing Market for Diabetes"). The increase in obesity related to reliance on fast food restaurant diets is predicted to lead to a decrease in life expectancy in the current century.[33]

Thanks, guys!

On top of that eating that food can make you feel depressed, as evidenced by Morgan Spurlock in his film *Super-Size Me*, when he ate nothing but McDonalds food for a month.

So, the next time you pull yourself up to your cheeseburger, have a Prozac with it.

Now read online, "Do Changes in Diet or Lifestyle Prevent or Treat Diabetes?"[34]

Chapter 18: Some of Us Physicians Actually Care About their Patients

George Bush appointed a veterinarian to run our nation's drug regulatory body, who was foolish enough to not disclose or divest of the pharmaceutical stocks he owned, and had to resign.

By <u>Doug Bremner, Contributor</u>

(Originally posted November 22, 2008, in *The Huffington Post*).

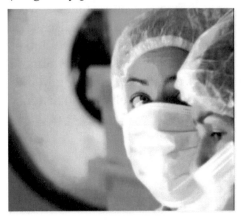

The drug maker Wyeth has issued a press release on the topic of preemption (see my post "No Redemption for Preemption"), as related to the case before the Supreme Court of Levine v Wyeth. Simply put, preemption strips away the rights of consumers to have redress in court if they have a toxic or fatal side effect from an FDA-approved prescription medication. The good people of Michigan have been struggling with this law for a decade, and now the drug companies are trying to push it through to become the law of the land.

Here is their press release.

"The public health is better served by having a single expert regulatory body making decisions about risks, benefits, and warnings - rather than an ad hoc system that could produce hundreds of conflicting results that would be impossible for manufacturers, physicians, and patients to reconcile or interpret. Such a system would undermine the careful balance struck by the FDA when making approval decisions. If Wyeth prevails here, it will only reinforce the principle that doctors are entitled to rely on FDA-approved professional labeling."

Ha! These are just a few of the reasons I think this argument is ludicrous:

How can you say that their viewpoints are carefully balanced, when they are guided by advisory panels of physician "key opinion leaders" that are usually on their payrolls as consultants, speakers, and/or advisory board members? And the fact that this advice is skewed can be shown by numerous examples, e.g., the fact that "expert guidelines" recommend the use of statins for the prevention of heart disease in women, when the evidence in the literature clearly shows that there is no benefit, only the risk of harm in the way of side effects? Preemption would effectively yank the protection that Americans get from the judicial branch of government and leave the executive and legislative branches in charge of protecting them. And what do they know about drug safety? Since the FDA's leadership is politically appointed, this would put the responsibility for guarding Americans in the hands of a small group of politicians who frequently benefit from donations from pharmaceutical companies. Witness how Dan Troy went from representing pharma to a job as chief counsel at the FDA, where he filed friends of the court briefs on behalf of FDA on the side of pharmaceutical companies whose medications had caused serious injury or death, on the rationale that since the FDA had approved the medications that they had a stake in the outcome. After this little jaunt he then tripped back to a cushy job in pharma.

Or here is another example. George Bush was so concerned about protecting us from dangerous prescription medications that he appointed a veterinarian, Lester Crawford, to run our nation's drug regulatory body, the FDA. I'm not sure if I feel comfortable having an expert on cows deciding which drugs end up in my medicine cabinet. Thankfully, Lester was foolish enough to not disclose or divest of the stocks he owned in the pharmaceutical industry, and precipitously had to resign.

Lately we have had to watch senators shouting at the FDA to tell him how much money they needed to keep America safe from Chinese milk or pet food or the latest drug disaster. The Director couldn't tell him, or more likely wouldn't, since his marching orders were to keep the budget small.

With the Prescription Drug User Fee Act (PDUFA) resulting in pharmaceutical companies paying more and more of the budget of the FDA, with PDUFA mandating that less goes to drug surveillance (watching drugs already FDA approved), the FDA is essentially working for them, so sure pharma thinks it will be a good idea to have a "single regulatory body", especially if it is working for them. And outside reviews of the FDA have said they are putting Americans at risk through their shoddy regulation of prescription medications.

Another argument against preemption is that taking the issue out of the courts removes a potential way to uncover fraud and deception in the management of data related to clinical trials, something that has come up not just once, but repeatedly, through the discovery process of ongoing trials.

And what is the argument about the law being "impossible to interpret." I have a suggestion for you; if a prescription medication is found to have an adverse outcome, warn doctors and the public, and if is too dangerous, take it off the market. That is what you are paying your doctors and scientists to do, analyze your data and evaluate risk/benefit ratios.

How about "...reinforce the principle that doctors are entitled to rely on FDA-approved professional labeling." Let me translate that one for you: Physicians, support this proposed ruling, because then you won't have to worry about covering your asses for prescription medication disasters.

I've got a thought for you, Wyeth. Maybe some of us physicians actually care about whether we are doing harm or good for our patients. What do you think about that?

Now read online, "Medication Treatment of Irritable Bowel Syndrome."[35]

Chapter 19: Side Effects of the Pharmaceutical Industry: Bullying, Corruption, Distortion, and Harm to Patients

(Originally posted November 25, 2008, in *Drug Safety & Health News*).

I am reading Alison Bass's book *Side Effects: A Prosecutor, a Whistleblower, and a Bestselling Antidepressant on Trial*.[36] Overall, it makes for a good read, a story about distortion of study results related to Selective Serotonin Reuptake Inhibitor antidepressants (SSRIs), and the corruption of leaders in the academic psychiatry field for the purposes of promoting profit for pharma.

Side Effects by Alison Bass

My only criticism is that at times it seems like there is too much narrative detail about taxi rides and other things that slowed the story down and are not directly relevant to the story flow.

However, I have to admit that the part I found most fascinating was the part about Martin Teicher, M.D., Ph.D., a psychiatrist I know personally, have had dinner with, read his papers and grant applications, and whose research interests overlap with mine (i.e., effects of childhood abuse on the brain).

Martin Teicher, M.D., Ph.D.

You see, Marty Teicher had the guts to say that Prozac (fluoxetine) could make some people (emphasis mine) suicidal, back in about 1990, at a time when we were all "listening to Prozac", or maybe drooling over Prozac, or whatever.

The "miracle drug" results in a two-point increase over placebo on a 56-point scale, which pharma now acknowledges, because it is off patent and they want to promote their new miracle drug Abilify (which is actually an antipsychotic, which will literally make you drool).

I actually skipped chapters to read the accounts of Dr. Teicher. You see I had heard that Eli Lilly had used rumors that he had had sex with a patient to silence him in expressing his views that SSRI antidepressant medications could increase suicidal thoughts. Not very good PR when they were launching their drug as the miracle cure for depression.

And they were pretty effective. Most of Dr. Teicher's recent research is on the effects of childhood abuse on the brain (NOT Prozac and suicidality).

I know that tune.

It's kind of hard to do research when your data gets subpoenaed before you have had a chance to go over it and fact check it. I know from experience.

In the schools I came from they call that bullying.

In Alison's book she gives a compelling narrative about an attorney for Eli Lilly named Nina Gussack who "softened up" Dr. Teicher and then hit him with accusations of a patient that he had had sexual relations with her. She spent two days deposing him after which he decided that he wouldn't testify again. Eli Lilly hired his ex-wife (leading her to move to Indiana for four years THE VERY DAY they deposed him, taking with her his kids), only to dump her when they had no further use for her.

Congratulations, attorney Nina Gussack, counsel for Eli Lilly, I hope you can sleep at night (try some Ambien).

From my reading of the book and my personal interaction with Dr. Teicher, I think the whole thing is a bunch of bullshit, Eli Lilly manipulating someone with borderline personality disorder for their own interests. In fact, the Massachusetts Medical Board found no evidence of any sexual relationship.

The only "evidence" they had was that Dr Teicher had given the patient a card saying "love marty" on her birthday and a pair of earrings valued at $3.50.

I write cards to my kids saying, "love dad." That doesn't mean I am having sex with them. Give me a f**king break.

Here is my card for Eli Lilly: "Thanks for making us suicidal! Love, Doug Bremner, M.D."

Chapter 20: Have a Placebo (Originally Posted as, Hey Buddy, Want a Placebo? How About a Statin for Your Wife?)

One article shows that half of doctors prescribe their patients placebos; another shows that 23% of patients on statins were women without heart disease.

By **Doug Bremner, Contributor**

(Originally posted November 28, 2008, in *The Huffington Post*).

This week there are a couple of related articles, one in *BMJ* showing that half of doctors prescribe their patients placebos, and the other in the *Journal of Empirical Legal Studies* showing that 23% of patients on statins were women without heart disease for whom there is no evidence of benefit.

The article in *BMJ* described how 62% of doctors think is it OK to give placebos, and half of doctors do so on a regular basis.[37] While only 2% reported using actual sugar pills, a larger number used over the counter analgesics (41%), vitamins (38%), antibiotics (13%) and sedatives (13%) as placebos. Most commonly they would describe the placebos to their patients as potentially beneficial medicine or treatment not typically used for their condition. Only 5% of doctors explicitly described them as placebos to their patients.

Want some pills? How about a placebo?

Comment: If doctors want to give placebos, they should use sugar pills, not drugs that could cause more harm than good. As I have written on this site before ("The Vitamins are Coming!"), vitamins increase the risk of osteoporotic fracture and are associated with an overall increase in mortality and heart disease, overprescription of antibiotics by doctors for conditions like viral infections that don't respond to antibiotics is increasing drug resistant strains of bacteria ("The Hospitals are Killing Us"), and sleeping pills and sedatives increase the risk of driving accidents, falls and confusion in the elderly ("Do We Really Need Eight Hours of Sleep Each Night?").

I would like to add to the list of placebos statin drugs for the treatment of women with risk factors for heart disease but without a history of heart disease. As I have previously pointed out ("Should I Give My Wife a Statin?" in a previous volume in this series), women with risk factors for heart disease but without a history of heart disease get no benefit from statin medications like Zocor, Lipitor, Pravachol and Mevacor, only side effects. Now it looks like the chickens are coming home to roost. As reported in bmj news, the makers of Lipitor may be called on the carpet for promotion of Lipitor to women for whom there was no benefit.[38] An article in the *Journal of Empirical Legal Studies* presents yet another meta-analysis showing that statins are not helpful for women without heart disease, and discusses the ethical and legal implications of promotion of a drug for a group for which there was no benefit, with a 12 billion dollar per year market for Lipitor (atorvastatin) and 9% of women over 70 without a history of heart disease being prescribed statins, and how this case highlights how preemption of state law by the FDA makes no sense (see "No Redemption for Preemption").[39] These facts boggle the mind. By combining data from men and women together and providing blanket recommendations for men and women, and omitting negative evidence for women, Pfizer (the makers of Lipitor) have driven sales in a group for which there is no benefit, and if anything, possibly harm. But anyway, the authors write:

If we are correct about omissions from Pfizer's advertising, then neither market forces nor FDA regulation has effectively regulated the mass marketing of Lipitor. The progression from the underlying scientific study of Lipitor, expressly reporting no benefit for women, to Pfizer's advertising of the world's best-selling drug while failing to disclose the absence of benefit for women raises grave concern about the FDA's regulation of drugs and drug company candor.

At a minimum, the FDA should use its authority to address massive questionable marketing. In addition, if consumers have not been properly informed about the efficacy of Lipitor or other drugs, reasonable remedies should exist for costs incurred associated with nondisclosure. Our review suggests the need for modified labelling, marketing, and information for physicians.

Not one of the studies that include women with a mixture of risk factors for heart attacks provides statistically significant support for prescribing Lipitor or other statins to protect against our cardiovascular end points. Pfizer's claims of clinical proof that Lipitor reduces risk of heart attack . . . in patients with multiple risk factors for heart disease, including family history, high blood pressure, age, low HDL ('good' cholesterol) or smoking does not appear to be scientifically supported for large segments of the female population.

Pfizer's advertising also does not disclose critical portions of the Lipitor FDA-approved label, which acknowledges the absence of evidence with respect to women.

The growing multibillion dollar statins market significantly contributes to increasing health-care expenses. Our findings indicate that each year reasonably healthy women spend billions of dollars on

> *drugs in the hope of preventing heart attacks but that*
> *scientific evidence supporting their hope does not exist.*

Here is Pfizer's response (read out loud with the accompaniment of Jacob blowing on his horn):

> *Statins have been called one of the most notable*
> *triumphs in modern medicine. The statin class has*
> *extensive data supporting a reduction in CV*
> *[cardiovascular] risk burden and Lipitor's ability to*
> *reduce cardiovascular morbidity and mortality has*
> *been demonstrated in 12 CV outcomes trials.*

> *Cardiovascular disease is a major cause of death in*
> *women as well as men and it ultimately kills as many*
> *women as men. However, onset of disease is delayed by*
> *some 10-15 years in women compared to men; thus, the*
> *National Institutes for Health (NIH) ATP III*
> *guidelines define age as a risk factor in women at age*
> *55, compared to age 45 for men. In addition, the AHA*
> *CVD Guidelines for Women were updated in 2007 and*
> *recommend that healthcare professionals should focus*
> *on women's lifetime heart disease risk, not just short-*
> *term risk.*

What a convoluted piece of logic. Women have heart disease, expert guidelines written by doctors and associations with financial conflicts of interest state that women without heart disease should be given statins, even in the absence of empirical evidence, only illustrates the fact that something is indeed rotten in the State of Denmark.

OK, now I am going to get out my crystal ball. Here it is...

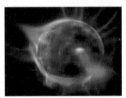

My crystal ball tells me that soon lawsuits will be sprouting out across the land as states claim that they were fleeced by Pfizer selling useless Lipitor to their Medicare and Medicaid patients. Check back for an update.

Now read online, "Are Calcium and Vitamin D Good for Your Bone Health?"[40]

[Update] Recently in the news has been the efforts by families to get justice in the courts for the asthma medication, Singulair (montelukast, see "If They Can't Kill You They Will Drive You Crazy"), and suicide, and running once again into the issue of FDA preemption of state law.[41]

Doug Bremner, M.D., is author of *Before You Take That Pill: Why the Drug Industry May be Bad For Your Health*

Chapter 21: Here Come the Four Horsemen of the Apocalypse, FDA Lawyers

This weekend was All Soul's Day, so I thought it appropriate that our own four horsemen of the apocalypse are ushering in our day of doom.

By **Doug Bremner, Contributor**

(Originally posted December 5, 2008, in *The Huffington Post*).

Well, this weekend was All Soul's Day, so I thought it appropriate that our own four horsemen of the apocalypse are ushering in our day of doom which will come in the form of the Supreme Court hearing the case of Wyeth v Levine this week, described as the 'Business Case of the Century' by NBC. As noted in a comment on pharmalot.com by Justice in Michigan, the only four people to comment on the Drug and Device Law website in favor of Wyeth's stance in favor of preemption (where FDA approval means you no longer have the right to a day in court if something goes wrong with a prescription medication) were current and former members of FDA counsel, Seth Ray, Sheldon Bradshaw, Gerald Masoudi and Dan Troy. Whadya know, they're all lawyers, which isn't surprising since only lawyers are in favor of preemption, and only FDA and pharma lawyers at that, some of whom are political appointees.

And so, I thought I'd bring them to you, the four horsemen of the apocalypse!

Four Horsemen of the Apocalypse

Sheldon Bradshaw, Dan Troy, Gerald
Masoudi, and Peter "the" Pitts

In the book of Revelations 6:1-8, the Lamb (Jesus) opens four seals, and with each one a colored horse and its rider jump out.

> I watched as the Lamb opened the first of the seven
> seals. Then I heard one of the four living creatures say
> in a voice like thunder, "Come!" I looked, and there
> before me was a white horse! Its rider held a bow, and

*he was given a crown, and he rode out as a conqueror
bent on conquest.*

Enter the first rider, Sheldon Bradshaw, former FDA chief counsel, who came online to say that complaints of FDA doctors (remember those guys who actually have some expertise in drug safety?) that preemption was a bad idea (as outlined in a report from Henry Waxman's office to the Supreme Court) shouldn't be taken seriously, as this was just a few grousers amongst "thousands of FDA employees", and that ruling against preemption would "open the flood gates" of over-warning and other evils.

*When the Lamb opened the second seal, I heard the
second living creature say, "Come!" Then another
horse came out, a fiery red one. Its rider was given
power to take peace from the earth and to make men
slay each other. To him was given a large sword.*

Enter the second rider, Dan Troy, former counsel for pharma who got a political appointment by Bush as chief counsel for the FDA, where he carried the large sword given to him by the pharma-supporting Republicans across the land, filing friends of the court briefs on behalf of drug companies involved in drug safety litigation, under the logic that if the FDA approved it they had an interest in fighting causes that claimed medication related harm. He was the brainchild of preemption, which truly will take peace from the earth. 'You come from the earth and to the earth you return.' Well in Dan's case he came from pharma, worked for a few years at the FDA pushing pharma interests, and then went back to a cushy job with pharma.

My, my! That revolving door is enough to make your head spin!

*When the Lamb opened the third seal, I heard the third
living creature say, "Come!" I looked, and there before
me was a black horse! Its rider was holding a pair of
scales in his hand. Then I heard what sounded like a
voice among the four living creatures, saying, "A quart
of wheat for a day's wages, and three quarts of barley
for a day's wages, and do not damage the oil and the
wine!"*

Enter the third rider, Gerald Masoudi! Who continued the work of his predecessor Dan Troy in carrying the sword of preemption across the land.

And our taxpayer dollars are paying the salaries of these guys? Wheat and barley, indeed.

> *When the Lamb opened the fourth seal, I heard the voice of the fourth living creature say, "Come!" I looked, and there before me was a pale horse! Its rider was named Death, and Hades was following close behind him. They were given power over a fourth of the earth to kill by sword, famine and plague, and by the wild beasts of the earth.*

I couldn't find a picture of Ray, so I substituted Peter Pitts, a former FDA official who now lobbies on behalf of pharma in favor of preemption through his PR firm and the Center for Medicine in the Public Interest. He is a better substitute for the rider of Death, since he consistently takes positions that put the profits of pharma over the lives of people taking their medicines. Peter uses their blog to take swipes at the likes of Drs. David Graham and Steven Nissen, whose only sins were uncovering risks of Vioxx and Avandia, which god forbid might cut into the profit margins of his beloved pharma.

[Update] See the *Justice in Michigan* web site which has been fighting preemption and trying to hold pharma accountable for many years.[42] Link provided by Henry Greenspan, PhD, of the University of Michigan.

Chapter 22: A Dissenting Opinion from the American College of Neuropsychopharmacology (ACNP) on Suicidality and Antidepressants

(Originally posted December 7, 2008, in *Drug Safety & Health News*).

This week I am in Scottsdale, Arizona, for the Annual Meeting of the American College of Neuropsychopharmacology (ACNP). We've had some memorable moments at the annual meetings of the ACNP (of which I am a proud member) which up until recently were held at the Caribe Hilton Hotel in San Juan, Puerto Rico. There is a rumor (which I am sure is false) that when the ACNP was founded back in the 60s they decided to have their annual meeting in Puerto Rico because the prostitutes were cheaper there.

The psychiatrists print out their research results on "posters" and pin them up on boards and then everyone walks around drinking wine and pretending to read the posters while catching up on gossip. And oh, we have some great gossip to catch up on. Usually, we are supposed to print the posters out from computers, but one year one of the psychiatrists drew the title of his poster with a crayon. Although the posters are supposed to represent research, another year one of the psychiatrists had a poster dedicated to the alleged corruption of another one of our august members. And then there are the numerous inquiries, investigations, accusations, and assorted phlegm sent to the group email list that livelies up our days.

Such fun!

We used to say that the struggles in academia were so great because the rewards were so small, but thanks to payola from Merck, Lilly, Pfizer, and friends, I guess we can't say that anymore! Cheerio!

Anyhoo, to the point of this post, my dissenting opinion from the official position statement of the ACNP on suicidality and antidepressants. For years the ACNP has been solemnly convening a committee every year to comment on a possible association between suicidality and antidepressants. Even five years ago when I viewed their report (before the more recent uproar over the topic) I saw their list of studies showing that in almost every case the rates of suicidality were doubled. I therefore concluded that the conclusions of my august fellow members were, frankly... bullshit.

Even now the ACNP continues to put its head in the sand and denies a relationship between antidepressants and suicidality.[43] But take a look at the people on the committee ruling on suicidality and antidepressants and you see conflicts abound with members taking speaking and consulting fees from drug companies. And it takes an *Infinite Reach* of the imagination to believe that antidepressants making you suicidal are no big deal, as was recently argued by one of the committee members on his NPR show, since it hasn't been shown that they will make you SUCCESSFULLY kill yourself since suicide is rare and no one has ever shown that something will make you more likely to successfully kill yourself.

Hey buddy, wanna buy some blue pills that are gonna make you think about killing yourself? Don't worry, in the end you won't actually do it.

[Update] I modified this post from the original slightly, but I want to point out that prostitutes can also be described as "whores," in keeping with the title of this series.

Chapter 23: Response to David Braff, M.D., Ph.D., President of the ACNP

Originally posted Dec 8, 2008, in *Drug Safety & Health News*)

I got a call yesterday from David Braff, M.D., Ph.D., President of the American College of Neuropsychopharmacology (ACNP) and Professor of Psychiatry at the University of California- San Diego (UCSD). It seems that some of my fellow ACNP members were miffed about my post, "A Dissenting Opinion from the ACNP on Suicidality and Antidepressants." To set the record straight, the post was meant in jest, although a number of sites picked it up as evidence of "sleazy" behavior of ACNP members. ACNP members don't routinely get drunk at poster sessions, as I implied. Although beer and wine are served there (as it is at the American Heart Association meeting, per Mrs. Bremner, and a number of other meetings) I hope they don't stop that practice because of my post! And the comment about the prostitutes being cheaper in Puerto Rico wasn't meant to imply that ACNP members currently frequent prostitutes. After all, they recently moved the meeting to Scottsdale, AZ. I'm sure the prostitutes there are very expensive!

As for the comments about the person who drew his poster title with a crayon and the other one who sat in a lawn chair next to his poster criticizing another ACNP member, well, what can I say?

On a more positive note, in response to concerns about the influence of the pharmaceutical industry on academic psychiatry through pharma funded educational activities and drug promotional talks,[44] and concerns that this compromises the patient-physician relationship, one of the ACNP members, Robert Golden, M.D., Dean of the University of Wisconsin Medical School (Madison), has instituted a policy to place signs in clinics alerting patients that their doctors may be receiving payments from drug companies and providing a form so that they can get more information.

The *Drug Safety and Health News* blog applauds the efforts of Dr. Golden which truly represents a move in a new direction.

COMMENTS

Susie (M-1, in Europe) wrote:

If anyone should have the right to question Dr Bremner's comparative expertise on the going rates asked by prostitutes at past ACNP congress venues, it's Mrs Bremner, M.D. But then Mrs Bremner obviously got the joke.

Why do high-raking members of the ACNP, as the English say, get their knickers in a twist about this? Don't they have anything more pressing to worry about and comment on, like, uuh, shills being KOLs?

Pease keep up the good work!

Now read online, "Herbs and Supplements for the Treatment of Depression – Do They Work and are They Safe?"

[Update] Dr. Braff actually admitted in that original phone call that he had heard a similar rumor about how the meeting was first started in San Juan. One of my beefs with the ACNP back then was how they published in their journal, *Neuropsychopharmacology*, a review of treatments for depression written by authors that were all paid members of the Advisory Board, including the editor of the journal, of a company called Cyberonics that made an implantable Vagal Nerve Stimulation (VNS) device. In the article they advocated for the use of the device for refractory depression, but failed to disclose that they were all on the advisory board of the company. Ironically, one of my main research areas is non-invasive VNS for the treatment of posttraumatic stress disorder, mild traumatic brain injury and opioid withdrawal.

Chapter 24: Wow! A Drug That Will Let Me Have Sex Once More a Month? Sign Me Up!

The authors of the study imply that menopause is linked to a decline in libido for women, and that they need to take a drug to correct that. But I'm not aware of any literature supporting this.

By Doug Bremner, Contributor

(Originally posted December 8, 2008, in *The Huffington Post*).

I don't care if it may give me breast cancer or heart disease. Thanks, APHRODITE Study Team!

APHRODITE Study Team? ROTFL!

I swear to God I am not making up this goofy study name.

I wonder if the study investigators ever got horny at one of their research meetings? Or by looking at their data?

Anyway, seriously folks. The results of the "A Phase III Research Study of Female Sexual Dysfunction in Women on Testosterone Patch without Estrogen (APHRODITE)" study published in the NEJM this week showed that if post-menopausal women who have a loss of libido put a testosterone patch on their arms that they will have satisfying sex once a month more than they are currently having, although there may be a risk of breast cancer or cardiovascular disease.[45]

I've got a tip for the marketers of this testosterone patch. If the women are having satisfying sex only once a month, and now they have it twice, why don't you say that the drug results in a 100% increase in satisfying sex!

Ha ha ha ha ha!

Okay, folks, all fun aside, let's look at the data. In this study 814 women were treated for 52 weeks with 300 or 150 microgram testosterone patches or placebo patches. There was an increase in "satisfying sexual episodes" of 2.1 in treated versus 0.7 for placebo, an increase that was statistically significant. There was about a 10% difference in scores on a sexual pleasure scale. 30% grew unwanted hair v 23% for placebo. Breast cancer was diagnosed in 4 out of 527 treated women and in none of the women on placebo.

That's right folks, sex once a month. And possible risk of getting breast cancer.

And a beard.

Nonconclusive results about cancer, you say. And Mrs. Robinson asks if she has anything to worry about.

Well, a recent <u>study</u> found that women who naturally had the highest testosterone levels (top 25%) had a two-fold increase in breast cancer compared to women in the lowest 25%.[46]

And another <u>study</u> found that postmenopausal women with elevated testosterone had increases in markers of inflammation and endothelial dysfunction, C-reactive protein (CRP) and endothelin, that have been associated with increased risk of atherosclerosis.[47]

And let's not forget the increased risk of heart disease and cancer associated with hormone replacement therapy (HRT) which I have written about before, and testosterone has to have a suspicion of similar risk.

The authors of the current study point to the fact that about a third of post-menopausal women have sexual dysfunction and imply that even the meager gain they eke out with their patch is worth it in terms of keeping them mans happy. However, they need to provide evidence for their implied claim that libido is killed by menopause and that women need to use a hormonal patch for that. They seem to hark back to the physician author of *Feminine Forever*, who implied that menopause was a disease to be treated with HRT, and that women became old crones, wrinkled and ugly, nasty, and incapable of sex, and that they needed HRT to treat this malady. Well, I won't belabor that now, and you can follow the links on this web site if you want to learn more about HRT, but I can tell you that controlled studies show it has no effect on libido, and only increases risk of cancer and heart disease. So there.

The authors imply that menopause is associated with an inevitable decline in libido for women, and that they need to take a drug to correct that. But I am not aware of any literature to support this conclusion, and if anyone has something, let me know. I mean, Mrs. Bremner seems to be doing okay so far.

As far as I know these testosterone patches are approved for hypogonadism in men with low testosterone but are widely used off label for loss of libido in men and women. The APHRODITE study results may be used to promote off label use of the patches. Stay tuned.

Now read online, "Should I Take Testosterone To Boost My Libido?"[48]

Chapter 25: Are Dermatologists Dippy?

(Originally posted January 5, 2009, in *Drug Safety & Health News*).

Rather than admit that one of their silver bullets, Accutane (isotretinoin), which was a "goose laying the golden egg" for F. Hoffmann-La Roche Pharmaceuticals (and their various "Roche" associates world-wide) to the tune of a billion dollars a year, could make kids kill themselves or cause grotesque birth defects in the kids of over half of women exposed when pregnant, dermatologists have sung themselves a lullaby that their magic pills don't make kids depressed, they actually make them better, by clearing up those ugly zits that drive them to despair. In what can only be described as a tragic collusion of conflicts of interest (COI) amongst their Key Opinion Leaders (KOLs) and willful denial amongst the lowly rank and file, they have decided to say "What? Me Worry?"

When the heat got turned up on Roche Pharmaceuticals after the son of Congressman Bart Stupak's (D-Mich) son Bart Jr. died of suicide while on Accutane in 2000, they got busy and called a "Scientific Advisory Board" meeting at the Ritz Carlton in Alexandria, Virginia, to opine on the topic of the relationship between Accutane treatment and depression. This meeting included figures from psychiatry like Kathleen Merikangas, PhD, Stuart Montgomery, PhD, and David Nutt, M.D., Chair of Dermatology David Bickers M.D., and psychiatrist Douglas Jacobs, M.D. Between the lot of them I think they have written about one paper total in the literature on the subject. But they did get paid a nice consulting fee for their efforts, of course.

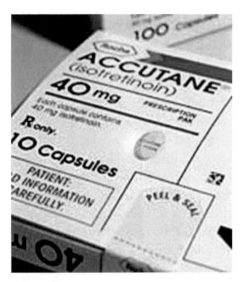

Accutane. Yum, yum!

Their conclusion? No relationship, of course.

I wasn't aware you were an Accutane expert, Kathleen!

I challenge them all to a debate. I'll fight them with one hand behind my back!

Fact is Accutane's efficacy for acne was discovered a decade before Roche put a patent on it, in a paper in *The New England Journal of Medicine*.[49]

I have communicated with two of the authors, both dermatologists, Frank Yoder, M.D., and Gary Peck, M.D.

Both of them agreed with my opinion that Accutane can cause depression in some individuals.

What is really sad about this whole sordid tale is how degenerated the so-called dermatology "literature" has become on the topic.

For example, the most commonly cited study to support the statement that acne is associated with depression, a study that has been cited several hundred times by dermatologists writing in the literature, involved only ten patients with acne and no comparison subjects.[50] No statistics were performed (obviously since there was no comparison group). Scores on the questionnaires for anxiety and depression were not related to severity of acne.

And the fact is that the rest of the literature isn't any better. Objective measures of acne do not correlate with severity of anxiety or depression. Acne does not cause major depression. It is simple as that.

Sure, kids worry about their zits and feel better when they go away, but the studies do not support the conclusion that acne causes major depression, and that treatment of acne cures depression.

In spite of this the manufacturer of Accutane, Hoffmann-LaRoche, has consistently downplayed the risks of suicide and depression and has denied a causal association.[51] The dermatology community has joined with the manufacturer in praising the merits of this medication for the treatment of acne which they describe as the "penicillin of dermatology." It took only 10 months for the FDA to approve Accutane for the treatment of cystic and nodular acne in May of 1982, however controversy has followed it from the time of its initial launch. In January of 1983 one of the authors of the first paper to describe the use of isotretinoin for the treatment of acne in 1977, Dr. Frank Yoder, wrote about the potential dangers of Accutane.[52] In 1990 Dr. David Graham of the FDA highlighted the inability of the Dermatological Medications Advisory Committee to the FDA to be impartial since it was made up entirely of dermatologists.[53] At that time, he stated that Accutane should be taken off of the market, mainly because of the risk of birth defects. Indeed, its use has always been curtailed or highly restricted in European countries, unlike the US where it is often prescribed for minor blemishes. Strong feelings about the utility of isotretinoin for the treatment of acne in the dermatology community, and forceful marketing by the manufacturer in the US, have caused a delay in awareness of the potential risks in the US. In 1998, the year that the FDA first approached Hoffmann-LaRoche about adding a warning related to suicide with Accutane to its label, the manufacturer ran an ad that stated, "Effective treatment of severe recalcitrant nodular acne minimizes progressive physical scarring, as well as negative psychosocial effects such as depression and poor self-image."[54] This was in spite of the fact that less than half of patients prescribed the medication actually had nodular acne. The FDA required that Hoffmann-LaRoche pull the ad.

In 2000 Congressman Bart Stupak's son, Bart Jr., committed suicide while on Accutane. Congressman Stupak called for congressional hearings on the safety of the drug and in September of that year the FDA called a Dermatologic Advisory Committee meeting on the topic. In November of 2001 an educational grant from Roche funded a supplement of the *Journal of the American Academy of Dermatology* on isotretinoin which followed the Scientific Advisory Board Meeting in Alexandria VA they held on the topic. The basic science-related articles focused on retinoids and the skin, essentially ignoring the large extant literature on retinoids and the central nervous system. Psychiatric side effects merited literally two sentences, and one article, written by one of Roche's hired guns, stated that there was no evidence for any association,[55] ignoring the reported challenge-rechallenge cases which have been cited in the pharmacoepidemiology literature as adequate in and of themselves to establish causality.[56] This led members of the FDA to write a letter of response, "in the interest of public health," admonishing the authors of these articles for the short shrift they paid to the issue of Accutane and psychiatric side effects.[57]

The degree to which dermatologists have thrown science and logic out of the window in order to protect their magic bullet is simply remarkable. For instance, in a 2004 article entitled "Myths of Isotretinoin Therapy"[58] "isotretinoin causes depression and suicide attempts" was listed as a "myth." The article went on to state that any risk needed to be "weighed against the increasing prevalence of depression among adolescents and young adults and the psychological impact of acne." [In fact, depression is not increasing amongst teenagers and acne has not been associated with clinical depression, rather only changes in self-esteem].

Here are some authentic mythic figures for you, Dr. Alcalay! And they don't have any pharmaceutical industry COIs!

Mythic figures

[Update] Accutane was taken off the market in June 2009, the manufacturer citing "business-related reasons." It continues to be sold in generic form as isotretinoin and cases of suicide and depression have been reported with generic use. Our article "Retinoic Acid and Affective Disorders: the evidence for an association" was published in the *Journal of Clinical Psychiatry*.[59] We also published "The neurobiology of retinoic acid in affective disorders"[60] in which we outline how retinoids could play a role in depression. More recently I published "Isotretinoin and Neuropsychiatric Side Effects: Continued Vigilance is Needed,"[61] which you can find online. I have also published a series of videos on TikTok (@jamesdouglasbremner) outlining the evidence for an association. This was established in 2000 by the FDA who reported 41 cases of challenge-dechallenge-rechallenge with Accutane and depression, which according to the *Textbook of Pharmacoepidemiology* is evidence in itself for a causal relationship.

My book *The Goose that Laid the Golden Egg: Accutane, the truth that had to be told* is now out and available on Amazon in the US and UK.

Now read online my rebuttal to points made by Roche and dermatologists about the association between Accutane and depression.

Chapter 26: Announcing Launch of DSM-V Shadow Team

(Originally posted January 7, 2009, in *Drug Safety & Health News*).

There has been some press that most of the members of the Diagnostic and Statistical Manual for Psychiatry-5 (DSM-5) task force are on the pharma payroll, but although sites like Public Citizen quote that 16/28 members are on the payroll, if you actually look at the list on the American Psychiatric Association (APA) web site there are only about six who don't report pharma ties, and these include NIH employees. Now a series of investigative reports from David Wilmer from the LA Times in 2003-4 showed that many scientists from NIMH were receiving consulting fees from pharma that they were not disclosing,[62] so maybe they aren't reporting it or they were too lazy to flee once the truth got out. The few others are employees of the APA, so it isn't clear what they are actually doing on the committee. Others have received educational grants and other perks from pharma, making pretty much everyone compromised, so it isn't surprising that a lot of people are worried about the potential corrupting influence that the pharmaceutical industry may be having on our beloved "bible" of psychiatry. Not to mention the fact that the members of the task force were required to sign confidentiality agreements that they wouldn't talk to anyone until the book was published. Oh, here is another one. They apparently decided that dissociative disorders don't exist, since they didn't even include that as one of their diagnostic groups. I guess there isn't a pill for that, and that's the whole purpose of this exercise, isn't it anyway? To create diagnoses that increase the number of under-identified Americans who need a psychotropic pill? Anyway, with all of these concerns, some of us psychiatrists when we were at the Annual Meeting of the American College of Neuropsychopharmacology in Scottsdale, AZ, recently decided to form...

DSM-V SHADOW TEAM!

... to express some dissenting opinions in the field of psychiatry. The idea is that we can "shadow" the "real" DSM-V task force and provide our own version of the DSM that is free of influence of pharma! (since we have either pissed off pharma by being to unsocial or ugly or asking embarrassing questions or maybe we farted at the wrong time or live in Canada so that none of us have significant financial conflicts of interest!)

I got the inspiration for this idea when I responded to an article on pharmalot.com about conflicts of interests in FDA Advisory Boards by volunteering to work (for free) on an FDA advisory board as I have no significant conflicts, and I pointed out that I have a lot to contribute (top in my field of PTSD based on ISI citations, 200 publications, drug trial expertise based on the last book I wrote). Henry Greenspan (Justice in Michigan) commented on pharmalot that maybe we could form our own "shadow" committees to parallel the FDA Advisory Committees for drug approvals that are so hopelessly corrupted by the fact that all of the members are paid consultants to pharma. I said I thought that was a wonderful idea.

I am not pointing out my own accomplishments for self-aggrandizement but to demonstrate without equivocation that when the pharma shills say that the best and brightest always consult to pharma that they are full of bullshit.

Pharma pick and groom their candidates and then highlight them at circuses like the Annual Meeting of the American Psychiatric Association which further increases the glitter of their "thought leaders."

We are a serious looking bunch in the picture, but, well this is serious business, I mean determining who gets psychiatric diagnoses and all. You'll notice I couldn't get any American psychiatrists to join the team. There are a few readers of the *Drug Safety and Health News Blog* that are on the "real" DSM-V work groups, and we tried to get them to come over from the dark side, but they just rolled their eyes.

Still time to reconsider guys! Won't have a chance like this for another ten years!

OK, let's get down to business. I am going to propose that one of the new diagnoses should be **Narcissistic Psychiatrist Syndrome (NPS)**. This syndrome is characterized by:

- Inability to look patients (or anyone else for that matter) directly in the eye.
- Delusional belief in the ability of psychopharmacology (as opposed to therapy) to heal all woes.
- Inability to discuss emotions or feelings, whether in self or others
- Inability to perform self-reflection.
- Difficulty answering direct questions without somehow turning it around to the questioner.
- Feelings of entitlement
- Inability to take blame.
- Gravy spots on the tie
- Tennis shoes and jacket with patches on the elbows; pipe

Here is another one, **Deviant Drug Rep Syndrome (DDRS)**

- Commonly lies to people while looking them straight in the eye.

- Compulsion to engage in risky behaviors associated with driving up drug sales (e.g., risky sexual behavior (possibly in doctor's offices))
- Inability to reflect on the consequences of one's actions.
- Cries out loud in joy when sites like pharmalot close down saying things like 'that will certainly make my job easier!'
- Incongruent emotional responses: e.g., persistently perky and cheerful behavior even in situations where sadness or other emotions are appropriate.

Which brings me to my next diagnosis, **Pharmalot Withdrawal Syndrome (PWS)**. I must say that my experience working with adult survivors of childhood abuse helped me in the recognition of this disabling disorder. You see, back in 1993 when I was working in the Mental Hygiene Clinic (as they used to call it) of the West Haven CT VA, I wanted to set up a program for research of childhood abuse survivors. None of the other psychiatrists were even willing to *ask* their patients if they had been abused for fear of the fact that they might crumble into dust if asked. So, I had to do the evaluations for them and offer to do a group to treat these patients once identified. One of the persons I screened said that he had been in treatment with the state community mental health for 30 years and no one had ever found his problem and on the first visit to the VA the doctor (me) doing the screening had found his problem just by asking if he was abused as a child! (He was) I ran the group with a nurse who grew up in an Amish family and had been sexually abused in childhood. We ran the group for two years and at the end of the time decided that the group should come to an end. Every week for the next year though the patients kept coming back to my office on the day and time we held the group. Well, that is how I feel now about pharmalot. Anyway, enough sentimentality, and on to the Shadow Team's DSM-V criteria for **PWS**!

- Feelings of sadness, anger, or tearfulness when contemplating the closure of pharmalot.com
- Obsessive internet activity involving reading comments about feelings of outrage related to a pharma HR exec who

took a helicopter to work while rank and file employees were being laid off.

- Having feelings of attachment to people you've never met who use false names like 'Atlex' and 'Former Pharma Exec.'
- Checking email inbox obsessively for pharmalot feeds
- Fantasizing about Ed Silverman's laptop

[Update] You may notice that the members of the Shadow Team are literally... in shadows. And since this original post I have put black boxes over their eyes to further shield their identities. That's because what was originally supposed to be taken as a joke got picked up by *New York Times Magazine* as a group that was literally going to shadow the workings of the DSM-5 task force. That and the fact that my fellow academic psychiatrists lack a sense of humor led to a whirlwind that resulted in the members of the task force... saying they no longer wanted to be on the task force.

Chapter 27: Pimping for Neurontin

(Originally posted January 9, 2009, in *Drug Safety & Health News*).

This has been quite a year for disturbing revelations about the corruption of the medical literature by pharmaceutical company interests. I wrote previously about ghost writing by Merck and others (see "Why Don't They Just Pay Us to Swallow Their Pills?"), and how papers were produced by drug companies that said, "insert author here" and then they went out and shopped around for an author at an academic institution. Academics are always worried about damage to their reputations, but in these cases, what can you say...?

I previously wrote about a study showing that the overwhelming majority of negative trials never get published while the positive ones always do, which leads to a false sense of the efficacy of the drug. The worst extreme of course is the sorry example of trials of SSRIs in kids where multiple studies of Paxil (paroxetine) were "shoved in the desk drawer" as we say here in the industry, and a bs campaign to get kids on Paxil was launched.

In the study I previously wrote about on suppression of the literature on antidepressants if you only looked at the medical literature, you would think that 94% of the studies show that antidepressants work, when in fact only 51% were positive.

I remember a couple of years ago standing at a poster with a glass of wine in my hand at the Annual Meeting of the American College of Neuropsychopharmacology (ACNP) which presented similar data (maybe it was the same study). Someone from pharma commented that you can't get negative data published. Well, that is a lot of hooey. You can get data published somewhere. For instance, *Psychopharmacology Bulletin*, where I am an Associate Editor, and that publishes its stuff online, makes a policy of taking in negative clinical trials.

Btw someone at the ACNP got miffed I think about my post on the ACNP and called and left a message asking what I "meant" by my post. I'm not sure if he was asking about my dissent from the ACNP's opinion that antidepressants can't make you suicidal (which they have faithfully affirmed for the past decade) or that the whores in Puerto Rico are cheaper than those in the States. Or that someone drew their poster title with a crayon. All statements I think are fairly straightforward and equally true (or at least in the case of #2 used to be, who knows with this volatile marketplace). Anyhoo I will keep you updated on the goings on.

In this week's *NEJM* there is an editorial about the promotion of Neurontin (gabapentin) for off label uses ranging from bipolar disorder to neuropathic pain. This editorial includes references to online documentation of how data was suppressed and manipulated, marketing tactics were used to illegally promote off label use, and academics, government, and the FDA either colluded or did nothing.

Wanna try some Neurontin?

Other news comes from an article by Ray Moynihan in *BMJ* showing that the pharmaceutical industry has used a strategy of "grooming" the Key Opinion Leaders (KOLs) (their terms, not mine) to promote their "message," and how they measure prescribing practices before and after a "KOL" gives a talk to check their impact on local prescribing practices, and then reward "good" KOLs with more talks with lucrative speaking fees and "drop" under performers.[63] Of course this unconsciously drives speakers to push their product. I for one went through this mill back in 2001 and was probably dropped for not performing and arguing with them about using their slides. I gave a talk last year for grand rounds at a med school and a friend of mine told me I was not "approved" by the drug company sponsors and therefore they had to scramble to find funds to pay for the talk. More news from the *BMJ* article is that there are organizations that offer to "manage" your "KOLs," like kolonline.com. You can read for yourself, but they basically offer their services to drug companies to manipulate or control KOLs to deliver the "right" message to the other docs who will follow their lead about how to prescribe. They offer to "validate and manage" the KOLs and "identify rising stars" (sounds like grooming young girls to participate in prostitution to me).

Key Opinion Leader (KOL) website

[Update: One of the ACNP members who accused me of being a hypocrite for signing a letter of support for the former chair of my department related to undisclosed conflicts of interest who landed on the front page of *The New York Times*[64] and who wrote a poster with a crayon about said chair he presented at the ACNP meeting, Barney Carroll, M.D., has since died. The journalist who wrote that article for the *NYT* later bailed me out when my university banned me from identifying myself as one of their faculty, even though I had tenure. It was over a joke letter I wrote for a fellow blogger on university letterhead. The reporter asked why I was punished for using letterhead when my chair used it to write what amounted to a press release on the safety of paroxetine for pregnant women and said he was writing an article on the topic. The dean at the time quickly reversed their position. My chair was eventually fired but went on to chair departments at other universities. The journalist who wrote the article was Gardiner Harris, who was later sent as a correspondent to India, where his children developed pulmonary diseases as a result of the high level of air pollution in the large cities there. After that, he returned to the US and apparently has retired. Gardiner, in my opinion, who is part of the Vanderbilt family, like the CNN correspondent, Anderson Cooper, represented the best of the reporting on the corrupting influence of Big Pharm on the field of psychiatry.]

Chapter 28: Spurious Advances in Antipsychotics, Indeed

(Originally posted January 12, 2009, in *Drug Safety & Health News*).

An article from the Jan. 3 2009 issue of *The Lancet* used a meta-analysis to show that so-called first generation antipsychotics (FGAs) and second generation antipsychotics (SGAs) are not that much different in terms of efficacy, safety, and side effect profiles.[65] The purported superiority of SGAs for negative symptoms and fewer side effects for SGAs were primarily the results of comparator studies that put them up against high dose haloperidol.

I have been reading a book called *Hooked: Ethics, The Medical Profession and the Pharmaceutical Industry*[66] by Howard Brody, M.D., Ph.D., of the University of Texas, Galveston, which I highly recommend as an interesting book that adds a lot even for those of you who feel you are "read out" on this topic, and this episode of comparing new drugs to old drugs given at doses that cause more side effects without providing more efficacy (which is stacking the deck in favor of the new drugs) is a pharmaceutical industry tactic that he identifies, although this is the first time we have heard of it as applied to antipsychotic "life-saving drugs."

Psychiatrists moved en masse from the FGAs to the SGAs largely because of concerns about tardive dyskinesia, extra pyramidal side effects, and what may have been a misguided belief that these drugs worked better, fueled by pharmaceutical marketing. As the paper shows, most studies in the literature were found to be using high dose haloperidol (7.5 mg/day) (Haldol) as the comparison drug, which biased the trials in favor of showing a better side effect profile for the newer drugs. When studies using lower potency first generation drugs were focused on, the differences in safety and efficacy were considerably diminished. Specifically, the SGA drugs as a whole were not seen to be specifically better for negative symptoms of schizophrenia, which does not support marketing claims to the contrary. The drugs that were better for negative symptoms were also equally better for positive symptoms and depression. Although clozapine, olanzapine (Zyprexa), and risperidone were marginally better for extra pyramidal side effects, which is largely why psychiatrists moved so heavily into SGAs in the first place, the effects were not large, and there were no significant differences for the other SGAs. The only SGAs that were shown to be better for psychotic symptoms than low dose FGAs were amisulpride (Solian, Sultopride), clozapine (Clozaril), olanzapine (Zyprexa) and risperidone (Risperdal). These drugs, however, caused more weight gain than haloperidol (but not low potency FGAs). Only Amisulpride and sertindole (Serlect) were better for quality of life. Aripiprazole (Abilify) was only better for depression and quetiapine (Seroquel) was better for positive symptoms and depression. Sertindole (Serlect), ziprasidone (Geodon), and zotepine (Zoleptil) were not better for any symptom area.

The recent CATIE study compared SGAs to the FGA perphenazine (Trilafon), and found that most of them were not better for efficacy or side effects, only olanzapine had a longer time to discontinuation (the primary outcome) and clozapine was better for symptoms.[67] However, clozapine has bothersome blood monitoring requirements because of the risk of aplastic anemia, and olanzapine has some worrisome diabetes risks. What was most amazing about the CATIE study, however, was the fact that half of people stopped taking their meds after a couple of months, which indicates that people feel really lousy on these drugs.

The article was accompanied by an editorial by Turner and Horton entitled "The Spurious Advance of Antipsychotic Therapy" in which the authors said that psychiatrists had been "beguiled" (presumably by the pharmaceutical industry) into believing that the SGAs were superior[68] (a point highlighted by others like Vera Sharav of the Alliance for Human Research Protection (AHRP).[69] Although I wouldn't agree with the emphasis that there is *no* difference between these drugs, it is true that the safety and efficacy of these drugs have been greatly distorted, that we should stop using the distinction of SGA-FGA or talking about unique profiles of "atypicals." In addition, it is unclear if the extra cost of these drugs justifies their use when there is an increased risk of obesity and diabetes with not that great of an advantage for extra-pyramidal side effects. Certainly, for the drugs not better than low potency FGAs there is not.

Guess we got duped by pharma. Yet again.

Sigh.

Now read online, "Should We Be Giving Antipsychotic Drugs to the Elderly?"[70]

[Update: The second-generation antipsychotics are now commonly used, and first generation not used as often, including in my own practice of psychiatry. In retrospect, while the second-generation drugs were on patent, a lot of hype was required to justify the considerable increase in expense. These days, the drugs are off patent, and used for the marginally better side effect profile. Non-compliance with these drugs continues to be high.]

Chapter 29: More on Disclosures and Response to Criticisms

(Originally posted January 14, 2009, in *Drug Safety & Health News*).

Bernard Carroll, M.D., has pointed out on several occasions on the internet that I signed a letter in support of Charles Nemeroff, M.D., Ph.D., to the *Wall Street Journal* in 2006 after the journal wrote a critical article regarding nondisclosure of conflicts of interest[71] in a paper about Cyberonics, and he has been critical of me as condoning bad behavior and therefore being therefore "no better" than others. The fact that the authors essentially comprised the Scientific Advisory Board of Cyberonics should have been disclosed in addition to other sources of funding and potential conflicts. At the time it was stated to be a mistake which is why I signed the letter. Since then, there have been other reports of non-disclosures that I have written about on this site and elsewhere, so that in retrospect it probably was not a good idea. In 2006 I was writing my book, *Before You Take That Pill: Why the Drug Industry May Be Bad For Your Health,* which is critical of the excessive influence that the pharmaceutical industry has on research and academic physicians, so my more recent writings on this site and others criticizing pharma influence is nothing new. I have previously posted about disclosure of my own conflicts of interest (which are posted at the top of all of my sites). Although I have consulted and given lectures in the past that were funded by industry I do not do so now and have not for the past two years and have not had any research funded for the past three years, although I did previously.

[Update] I'm not really sure what I was apologizing for here. I was a faculty member under this person and hardly independent and after 20 other faculty members signed this letter, I basically took him at his word that he made a mistake. I was dependent on promotion from my chair and to not sign would have been career suicide. Carroll was in fact the guy sitting in the lawn chair at the ACNP and his poster was about Charles Nemeroff, his nemesis since the time when he was

Chair of the Psychiatry Department at Duke University School of Medicine in Durham, North Carolina, and Nemeroff who was a junior faculty member there (I was a medical student there at the time) who wanted his job. Nemeroff gave Duke an ultimatum and ended up going to Emory University School of Medicine in Atlanta, Georgia, where he became the Chair of the Psychiatry Department, where I eventually (after a residency in psychiatry and several years as a junior faculty member at Yale) ended up as a Professor. Another one of the pot-shot criticisms I took back in 2008 was that I did research on Paxil. I've done a lot of research on the effects of antidepressants on the brain over the course of my career, including a publication on the effects of paroxetine (Paxil) on functional brain responses to traumatic scripts in patients with posttraumatic stress disorder PTSD published just this year,[72] and our finding that paroxetine increases volume of a brain area involved in memory called the hippocampus based on MRI[73] is one of the most important findings of my career and was a direct application of research coming from animal studies, a paradigm of "translational research." In retrospect the criticism about doing research on paroxetine was complete bullshit.

Chapter 30: Put It Back

(Originally posted January 14, 2009, in *Drug Safety & Health News*).

I have been mulling over my conversation with David Braff, M.D., PhD, President of the American College of Neuropsychopharmacology (ACNP), about how my fellow ACNP members were miffed about my post "A Dissenting Opinion from the ACNP on Suicidality and Antidepressants." Although I applaud the efforts of psychiatrist blogger Daniel Carlat, M.D., to provide medical education that is not supported by the pharmaceutical industry (for those out of the game pretty much ALL education is industry funded, often through private companies that are front organizations for pharma), I thought that his essay in *The New York Times*[74] about being a reformed industry funded speaker was a bit of a disservice since it focuses on psychiatry and glosses over the vast extent of pharma payments to academic physicians for talks and consulting that plays a very real role in disrupting the physician patient relationship.[75] After all, after the recent broo ha ha at Emory[76] the main thing is that my colleagues in other departments like Medicine are grumping about how the publicity is going to affect their outside income from pharma. Anyhoo, I was a bit miffed when Dr. Carlat called my former Chair at Emory Dept of Psychiatry names. I mean, I may make fun of organizations like the ACNP, but I don't call people names (usually). It was a deliberate decision not to name the person at the ACNP who drew his poster title with a crayon and the other one who sat in a lawn chair next to his poster criticizing another ACNP member in my recent post on the ACNP. Dr. Carlat, on the advice of his advisory board, took back his comment, but then when the publicity came out, regarding his previous comment he said...

All this talk about conflicts and name calling is stressing me out. Time to take a breather at one of my favorite web sites, lolcats.

Chapter 31: We Fly En Sel Drugz, Eet Rat

(Originally posted January 15, 2009, in *Drug Safety & Health News*).

I remember one time sitting out on the deck of my family's house on Puget Sound talking to my father and my brother and telling them that the people in academics didn't have a sense of humor and they told me I should work in a different field. That seemed extreme to me at the time but in retrospect I think they were probably right. That is why I am saddened to have lately written such boring and unhumorous posts as my responses to the ACNP and others in which I didn't use any humor in order to not piss them off any more than they are already.

A lot of people have written to me saying that I had "courage" or similar things to express things directly. Fact is that academics take themselves too seriously, don't have a sense of humor, emphasize loyalty, and live in fear of their colleagues and of various outside forces. Come to think of it, it reminds me a lot of the mafia from my wife's native Sicily. Like them, academics are a group that share in common something to hide, namely large payments from pharmaceutical companies that they privately justify as payment for services in drug development but that they nevertheless don't want to be publicly known.

Psychiatrists generally attribute criticism to scientologists or anti-psychiatrists and use that tactic to blow them off but my colleagues in medicine just go with a sense of self entitlement. One of the readers of the *Drug Safety & Health News* was a physician in another department at Emory who complained that he went to his computer every morning and got an email called "Before You Take That Pill." He also complained that the publicity over pharma payments to physicians threatened his ability to get income from giving lectures funded by the pharmaceutical industry. So, I just took him off my email list and he is happy now. Reminds me of a psychiatry consult I once did on an inpatient who had a heart attack and was depressed. He was obsessing about a picture in a heart education book they had given him that had a diagram of how a blood clot had obstructed a coronary artery. My "treatment" was to tear the page out of the book. Worked wonders.

I have been reading a <u>book</u> about the relationship between the pharmaceutical industry and academic medicine[77] and I am coming to the conclusion that ANY so-called education funded by pharma is suspect, and that physicians should go back to the old system of paying for their own god damn education. Or read a book for Christ's sake.

Anyhoo, I digress and as usual I forgot what I was talking about. Oh, yes. Lolcats. Lolcats are always there to come to the rescue when we lose our sense of humor or get an exaggerated view of ourselves. Lisa Van Syckel told me that the quote from Senator Charles Grassley (R-Iowa) is:

> *If you swing a cat around by the tail, you will hit*
> *someone from the pharmaceutical industry.*

Swing a cat by its tail.

I had to puzzle over that for a while like one of the Koans that my beloved deceased mother used to enjoy and had to ask Lisa what that meant.

"Well, it just means that there are a lot of people in the pharmaceutical industry."

Sometimes things that are true are also so simple that you can't recognize it if it is right in front of your face. What was your face before you were born?

I have been mulling over that this week, as well as the effects of pharmalot withdrawal, which has been under consideration as a new psychiatric disorder by our DSM V Shadow Team. Related to that in an interview after the closure of pharmalot with pharmalot's Ed Silverman by BNET journalist Jim Edwards (who incidentally prompted my post about facebook "Will You Be My Friend?" after he hurt my feelings by asking why I wanted to "friend" him) Ed said that his favorite post was one about Pfizer VP for HR Mary McCleod taking a helicopter to work in Manhattan every week when the rank and file were being laid off and there was cost cutting all around. That prompted a fascinating ongoing string of comments from Pfizer employees and "stockholders" expressing their outrage interspersed with comments from people like Justice in Michigan and Jaynesday saying "Hey look, you have a conscience like us" which they of course ignored. Lisa also told me that when Pfizer employees were protesting outside of corporate headquarters in NJ that they put a giant inflatable rat outside. Here he is at another gig outside the International Longshoreman's Union in Brooklyn.

Inflatable rat

Of course, that brought to mind Sen. Grassley's comment so of course
I had to photoshop it, and here it is.

I WANZ GO SEL DRUGZ

DON LET THET RAT LEVE BIFOR A GET THER!
LOL!

Chapter 32: Effects of Zoloft (Sertraline) on Childhood Anxiety are Incredible, Indeed

(Originally posted January 25, 2009, in *Drug Safety & Health News*).

A quote from a physician describing the results of study published this week in the *New England Journal of Medicine* on the effects of Zoloft (sertraline) or cognitive behavioral therapy (CBT) or a combination of the two on childhood anxiety disorders,[78] describing the results of the study as "incredible", lead me to take a look at the study myself to see if this claim was in fact, er, credible, or more of the same fare we have been dished out regarding the use of SSRIs in children, such as the infamous Study 329 of paroxetine (Paxil) in the treatment of depression in teenagers.

Sad Face with Smiley Faces

The current study looked at 488 children between the ages of 7 and 17 years who had the diagnosis of separation disorder, social phobia, and/or generalized anxiety disorder (GAD). They received 14 sessions of cognitive behavioral therapy, sertraline (up to 200 mg per day), a combination, or placebo for 12 weeks. The authors reported a score of "much improved" or greater on the Clinical Global Impression-Improvement Scale in 81% of kids treated with combination drug/therapy, 60% for CBT alone, 55% for sertraline, and 24% for placebo.

However, using a categorical outcome like "improvement" can be misleading. Take the example of the infamous Study 329 which pointed to the outcome of a 50% or greater improvement on the Hamilton Depression Scale as evidence for benefit of paroxetine in the treatment of childhood depression. The original primary outcome of the 329 Study was improvement in depression as measured by the Hamilton Depression Scale. The authors later "changed their minds" about what they should focus on, a fact that came out later. It is important to define a primary outcome in advance, otherwise there is a tendency to fish around for a positive result, which may lead to something that is just a fluke being interpreted as due to something real.

In the sertraline/CBT study, the authors (as far as we know) had "improvement" as their primary outcome. However, improvement can be misleading. Let's focus on the sertraline treated group alone, since CBT has no side effects and I am fine with people using CBT, and since the authors did not report a statistically better outcome of the combination therapy compared to CBT alone (although the press releases trumpets, incorrectly, that the combination is better). Say the primary goal is to run a mile in 10 minutes (or whatever, I say as I sit on the couch). If out of 100 people running, people wearing green shirts do it, on average, in 9 minutes 45 seconds, and people wearing red shirts do it in 10 minutes 15 seconds, you could have a result where 60% of the green shirts make the goal versus 25% of the red shirts, which sounds like a big deal, even though there is only a 5% difference in their times.

So, let's look at these studies. In the case of Study 329,[79] 66% of kids treated with Paxil (paroxetine) were "much improved" or better as measured by the Clinical Global Impression Scale (CGI) [criteria used in the Zoloft study] versus 48% of those treated with placebo, which they reported as statistically significant. Not bad, you say, however they did not find a significant change in their primary outcome, and to report the study as positive is a violation of the rules of clinical trials, as pointed out in a subsequent letter to the editor. In fact, if you look at the actual data, the Ham D score went from a baseline of 19.0 in both groups, to 8.2 in the paroxetine group and 9.9 in the placebo group, a paltry 3% difference in a 56-point scale which was not reported as significantly different because it was not, well, different.

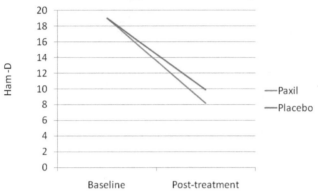

Effects of Paxil on Depression in Teenagers – Study 329

When you actually look at the data, the effects are not that great

Study 329 Paxil in Children with Depression

So now let's turn to the "incredible" results of this week's study of sertraline (Zoloft) in kids. Although there was a difference in "responders" based on much improved on the CGI of 60% versus 24% for placebo, when you look at the actual data, the Pediatric Anxiety Scale, a 30 point scale, went from 18.8 at baseline to 9.8 in the Zoloft group, and from 19.6 to 12.6 in the placebo group, a difference of 9%, again, not reported as statistically significant because it was not, in fact, very different. In fact, only CBT (not combination) was better than placebo on the anxiety scale. My clinical methodology experts tell me that a study is pretty weak if it only shows a positive outcome on a single categorical (yes/no) outcome and not on the continuous (multi-item) scale. And the combination group had no comparison group. Just, here is your psychotherapy (66% get better), and now open up your mouth and let me give you a yummy blue pill that Mommy says is going to make you better (80% get better).

Effects of Zoloft on Anxiety in Children

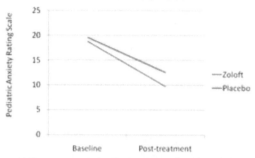

When you actually look at the data, the effects are not that great

Effects of Zoloft on anxiety in children

OK, dictionary time.

incredible Pronunciation [in-kred-uh-buhl] adjective

1. so extraordinary as to seem impossible; incredible speed.

2. not credible; hard to believe; unbelievable: The plot of the book is incredible.

[Origin: 1375-1425; late ME incredibilis]

Related forms incredibility, incredibleness, noun

incredibly, adverb

Incredible, indeed.

COMMENTS

John Grohol wrote on Psych Central on November 3, 2008

Bremner's off-the-cuff analysis wrongly suggests the current researchers had no specific outcome objectives.

He also states that I did not focus on the combination CBT and Zoloft group, which had an 80% response rate, which was statistically significant and, in his opinion, clinically significant. You can read the rest of his post here.

As I will write on his site:

I did not mean to imply that there was no specific outcome. By saying they used 'much improved' I understand that you could take it that way, but I very much know that much improved corresponds to a 2 on the CGI [very much improved is a 1, so subjects had either a 1 or 2 post treatment] which is a validated scale used throughout clinical trials, by myself and others. And I have no reason to doubt that it was chosen a priori as the primary outcome measure, although I guess we can wait for the lawyers and their experts to go digging through the emails and files as they always inevitably seem to do, to attempt to prove a change in primary outcome [these days with clinicaltrials.gov primary outcomes are registered in advance]. However, my criticism was of using the CGI as the primary outcome in isolation, and that what I consider the more relevant Pediatric Anxiety Scale did not show a significant change (time by treatment interaction) for Zoloft OR combination compared to placebo. Also, that the combination group had no comparison (i.e., CBT plus placebo) and the combination group knew they were getting Zoloft. Having categorical (yes/no, i.e., CGI) and not continuous (anxiety scale) outcomes makes it, not necessarily a negative trial, but not strong either, and certainly not "incredible" as described in the press.

[Update] Mrs. Bremner and I published a letter to the Editor with our critique of this study.[80]

To the Editor:

We believe that the conclusion of a recent study that sertraline and/or cognitive behavioral therapy is efficacious for childhood anxiety should be interpreted with caution. The authors reported the percentage of patients with "much improved" or greater on the Clinical Global Impression-Improvement Scale. However, using a categorical outcome like "improvement" can be misleading. Although there was a difference in "responders" based on this outcome, on the arguably more clinically relevant continuous measure, the 30-point Pediatric Anxiety Scale, scores went from 18.8 at baseline to 9.8 in the Zoloft group, and from 19.6 to 12.6 in the placebo group, a difference of 9%, that was not reported as statistically significant, and is in fact consistent with the large placebo response and weak effect of antidepressants seen in previously reported studies in children. In fact, only CBT alone was better than placebo on this scale. In the absence of a change in the continuous measure of anxiety the current study should not be interpreted as definitive evidence of efficacy of sertraline for childhood anxiety.

James D Bremner, M.D.,

Emory University School of Medicine and Atlanta VAMC

Atlanta, GA 30306

Viola Vaccarino, M.D., Ph.D.

Rollins School of Public Health

Emory University

Chapter 33: Doubling of Prescription Medication Use in Kids During a Three-Year Period

(Originally posted January 26, 2009, in *Drug Safety & Health News*).

There has been a dramatic increase in the number of children on prescription medications in the last few years, as Liz Szabo wrote today in *USA Today* "Number of kids on medication jumps alarmingly: Most of the illnesses related to obesity." From 2002-2005 there was a doubling of kids on prescription medications for Type 2 diabetes. There was also an increase in kids on medications for cholesterol, asthma, and ADHD. The article noted that diet and lack of exercise are responsible for the increase.

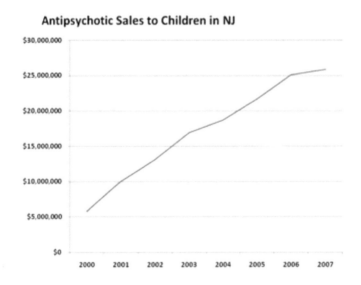

However, I don't think that our main-stream media are giving us very good advice about what we should be doing to help our kids avoid these trends. Maybe that is because us doctors doing the research are so muddled and mucked up with our preconceived notions, conflicts of interest, and various biases. One of the mainstream medias main recommendations are that we should choose a low-fat diet, but as others have pointed out, low-fat means substituting calories in the form of carbohydrates, which probably are worse in terms of inducing diabetes. There has been some discussion on this blog about the nature of fats, carbohydrates and cardiovascular disease and diabetes, and I have been reading some new books on the topic and will post on that later.

The Diabetes Prevention Program Research Group Study, however, did implicate diet and lack of exercise in Type 2 diabetes.[81] The study showed that at-risk individuals who met with a nutritionist who helped them change their diet and lifestyle (more exercise, less fat and saturated fat, more fiber) cut their risk of developing diabetes by 58%, even though they only lost 8 pounds on average. Prevention of diabetes with lifestyle intervention was better than medication (metformin), with a 58% reduction in new onset diabetes in at risk patients, compared to 31% for metformin. Eleven percent of patients on placebo developed diabetes in one year, compared to 8% on metformin, and 5% with the lifestyle intervention (DPPRG 2002). Patients on metformin had more gastrointestinal side effects than the other groups.

Maybe we should do a study where people simply spend an hour every night gazing at the moon.

Viola Vaccarino wrote on November 4, 2008

The problem with these studies is that things go in tandem, e.g., exercise coincides with cutting down on sugar, and stopping smoking, etc., etc. I don't see why this is a problem. Lifestyle interventions cannot just address one component and not others. They go in tandem and probably also work in tandem. For example, you cannot do a study where you advise people about exercise and still let people smoke. It is unethical to not give them advice about smoking cessation.

Now read online, "A Growing Market for Diabetes."[82]

Chapter 34: Bad Baby! Take Your Risperdal!

(Originally posted February 2, 2009, in *Drug Safety & Health News*).

After posting about the increase in psychotropic drug use in children and commenting that doctors should stop giving antipsychotics to children without schizophrenia, I got some words of praise from Philip Dawdy at *Furious Seasons* and some interesting information from Lisa Van Syckel[83] who gave me a list of ages and drugs given to kids in New Jersey (NJ) which I found shocking, as well as data on antipsychotic drug sales to kids in NJ. Here are some examples of kids given antipsychotics in NJ:

- A months old infant on chloral hydrate (sleeping pill).
- A two-year-old on Strattera (ADHD psychotropic drug).
- A three-year-old on Methylin (methylphenidate, or Ritalin, a stimulant ADHD drug)
- A four-year-old on Concerta (extended-release methylphenidate for ADHD)
- A two-year-old and a three-year-old on Risperdal (risperidone).
- A three-year-old on Adderall (amphetamine salts)
- A two-year-old on Ativan (lorazepam) (sedative, sleeping pill)
- A three-year-old on Ritalin
- A three-year-old on Focalin (dexmethylphenidate, ADHD stimulant drug)
- A four-year-old on Zyprexa (olanzapine)
- A three-year-old on Paxil (paroxetine)
- A three-year-old on Seroquel (quetiapine)
- An infant on Valium (diazepam)
- A four-year-old on Ambien (zolpidem, a sleeping pill)
- A four-year-old on Prozac (fluoxetine)

Bad baby! Take your Risperdal!

Meanwhile sales of antipsychotic drugs to children continues to climb (data from NJ)

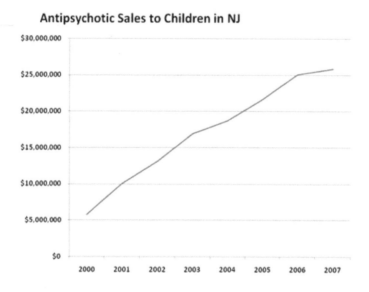

Shocking!

Come on guys! Here is some more free continuous medical education (CME) that is not funded by pharma! Babies don't sleep through the night, but they don't need a pill! Toddlers have tantrums but don't have bipolar disorder in need of antipsychotic drugs! It doesn't matter if three-year-olds don't concentrate because they aren't in school anyway and they don't need ADHD drugs! Three-year-olds don't develop "major depression!"

133

Stay tuned for more Alt CME.

Now read online, "When Should Children Be Given Antipsychotic Medications?"[84]

Chapter 35: How Much Ya Gonna Pay Me for Those Medical Guidelines?

(Originally posted February 3, 2009, in *Drug Safety and Health News*).

There is an underline in this week's issue of *JAMA* by Drs. Sniderman and Furberg on the issue of medical guidelines,[85] something that I have written about before (see "Delays and Suppression of Clinical Trial Results"), for example about how the National Cholesterol Education Panel (NCEP) came up with guidelines that would put 25% of the American population on statins, even if they were well. As I have written about before, men with few risk factors for heart disease and women without heart disease have no demonstrable benefit from taking statins, unless you have a relative who owns stock in drug companies. Also, countries like New Zealand (or any other rational country for that matter), who would put half as many people on statins per their guidelines, have NO differences in heart disease mortality from the US. Which means that there is something definitely wrong with this picture.

Rumors have it that Dr. Curt Furberg once received death threats for his audacious role in pointing out the dangers of drugs like Vioxx, and I have written in my book *Before You Take That Pill* quoting him.

DR. CURT FURBERG
Wake Forest University
Public Health Services Dept.

C-SPAN 2

2/19/05

"The [company] reps tell the doctors, 'You should follow these guidelines,' implying that you're not a good doctor if you don't follow these guidelines."

Dr Curt Furberg testifying to congress on problems with med guidelines.

In this week's editorial, they write:

> Doctors often feel entitled to, e.g., get lucrative
> speaking fees from the companies affected by the
> guidelines that they are writing, or to get freebies and
> dinners. But I think the American public is getting fed
> up. So, for the doctors out there, here is a free Bic pen
> that doesn't have any drug advertising on it.
>
> The anchoring authority of the guideline process is the
> belief that guidelines are evidence based, not opinion
> based, and therefore their conclusions flow directly
> from the conclusions of studies.

In other words, doctors assume (incorrectly) that guidelines are written by objective observers who are not serving as proxies for the pharmaceutical industry. In addition to conflict of interest issues, the writers point out that the guidelines do not undergo peer review, are not made available on the internet for public comment, are typically written by M.D.s with no epidemiologists or statisticians on the committees, inappropriately represent areas of uncertainty as definite, and serve as spring boards for doctors to go on to lucrative speaking careers funded by pharma based on the prestige of having been on the committees. They correctly point out that saying you consult to all drug companies and therefore do not favor any one of them in particular is not a valid argument. They argue for full disclosure of companies and amounts earned.

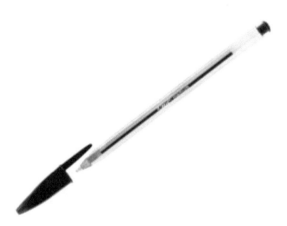

For all you do, this (plain) Bic's for you.

Hat tip to Brenda Patoine.

Now watch "Doug Bremner, M.D., on the Pharmaceutical Industry Part 1" on YouTube.

Chapter 36: I Don't Like Foxes, They Make Me Nervous: Doctors and the Pharmaceutical Industry

(Originally posted February 5, 2009, in *Drug Safety and Health News*).

In this week's edition of the *British Medical Journal (BMJ)* there are some articles on "Doctors, patients, and the drug industry" which include some typical "fair and balanced" he said-she said articles in which avatars like Marcia Angell (doctors should cut ties with drug industry) and our old friend from Yale Harlan Krumholz, M.D., (Hi, Harlan!) are trotted out against industry insiders who provide the "balance" by saying that pharma and academic doctors can provide an alliance to promote health (Yea!! Gimme a D!!) and that pharma educates consumers about drugs (Abilify my depression, pretty please!).[86] Let me tell you that doing an issue like this without letting a pharma person write a piece isn't possible (I tried) because it would kill ad revenue for the journal (has happened in the past) which is why you need to keep reading the *Drug Safety and Health News* to get the real story!

The Pharma Bandit

Anyhoo, these kinds of "balanced" editions are like letting the fox into the hen house! Kinda like the Prescription Drug User Fee Act (PDUFA) of 1992 when the retarded AIDS activists got co-opted to push legislation whereby for a fee of 576K to FDA per drug application that pharma could fund more FDA staff and speed drug approvals. There was a stipulation of a 3% increase in budget for the new drug application approval section of FDA per year, and since Congress froze the FDA budget that meant that they had to cut funding for approved drug surveillance. Translation: Once FDA approves a drug, you are on your own baby. And by letting pharma pay for FDA staff we let the fox into the henhouse.

Mmm. Smells Like Chicken... Cuz it IS Chicken! Yum!

However, although Harlan has accused me of doom and gloom it is not all that way in the view of the editorial staff of the *Drug Safety and Health News* blog. I liked the introductory article where Iain Chalmers was quoted as writing in the report from the Royal College of Physicians:

> *I do not blame industry for trying to get away with anything that is normally considered to be its primary purpose, which is to make profits and look after its shareholders' interests. It is our profession that has colluded in all of this and been prepared to go along with it: we are the people to blame because we need not have stood for it.*

Fiona Godlee, Editor of *BMJ*, said:

> *By "all of this" I assume Chalmers means the many*
> *ways in which drugs are promoted in the guise of*
> *science, education, and information: the misreporting*
> *of industry funded research, the use of ghost writers*
> *and key opinion leaders, the provision of free courses*
> *and conferences. His words echo Suzanne Fletcher's in*
> *the BMJ last year (2008;337:a1023,*
> *doi:10.1136/bmj.a1023). For these practices to flourish,*
> *doctors have had to at least acquiesce, if not actively*
> *take part, as researchers, guest authors, paid opinion*
> *leaders, and recipients of gifts and hospitality.*

Well, the Brits are getting it, I think, i.e., doctors should not shill for the pharmaceutical industry. Let's see if my American colleagues can get with it, although I don't think they are really there yet.

Anyone got a pen?

Hat tip to Marilyn Mann.

Chapter 37: This Just In: Breast Cancer Screening Found to Be Essentially Useless

(Originally posted February 9, 2009, in *Drug Safety and Health News*).

A certain SOMEONE that I know who is a healthy middle-aged woman had to undergo a colonoscopy cuz her gynecologist came up with a positive guaiac test (screening for internal bleeding). Only AFTER the scope did I start to wonder about if there could be false positives, and me 'n google learned that if you eat a lot of tomatoes you can come up 'n false positive, and since she is Yugoslavian (har, har) she eats a lot of tomatoes. Her physician SHOULD HAVE warned her of that. Doh! Now her mammogram got flagged for additional testing and I am starting to wonder (yup) could it be false positive?

That is why an article in this week's *BMJ* about breast cancer screening caught my eye.[87] Current recommendations state that women over 50 should get yearly mammograms, and pamphlets say that screening will save lives and decrease mastectomies, which, alas, is apparently not true. The article shows that one in 10,000 women will be saved from a death related to breast cancer if they get yearly mammograms. However, 5% of mammograms come up as false positives, meaning that women will have to wait for months with anxiety, coming back in for more painful and expensive tests, all for nothing. And what is more, over a ten-year period there is a 50% chance of a false positive. That means that women getting mammograms as recommended can flip a coin; heads you get a false positive reading, tails you don't.

And what is worse, if you are found to have a cancer in situ, which constitutes 20% of cases, that will likely lead to radiation, even though less than half of these cases will progress to a spreading cancer. Obtaining this information was described as like "trying to uncover a closely guarded state secret."

Which brings us to the fact that breast cancer screening has not been shown to have any effect on mortality. The implication is that for each life saved from breast cancer, there is one life lost due to the effects of radiation treatment for something like cancer in situ that would never have progressed anyway.

In other words, breast cancer screening is of little substantive value.

Arghhh!

Let's start making our list of useless screening procedures.

Hat tip to the Gary Schwitzer, *Health News Blog*.

[Update: Both Mrs. Bremner and I just got our second screening colonoscopy. I noted a statistic that colonoscopy screening reduced mortality from colon cancer, so it might be a good idea, especially if you have a family history of colon cancer, like I do. However, colonoscopy has a 95% sensitivity for colon cancer detection, which is not that much better than the 92% sensitivity of stool tests you can buy at the pharmacy for a few bucks. They (meaning the guys that make the big bucks off of them) say that colonoscopy is better because you can remove polyps in the process. Not sure why that would be true. I guess you can either drink a noxious drink that makes you poop yellow liquid for the colonoscopy prep, or you can fish around for your poop in the toilet to do the stool sample test. Your choice.]

Chapter 38: Multivitamins Useless for Postmenopausal Women, Surprise, Surprise

(Originally posted February 11, 2009, in *Drug Safety & Health News*).

This article just in from the Women's Health Initiative Study, published in this month's edition of the *Archives of Internal Medicine*, on the utility of taking multivitamins for postmenopausal women.[88] Now since the marketing staff of the *Drug Safety and Health News* blog have been conducting focus groups amongst the readers of the blog, we have learned that the average reader is a middle aged woman from Marin County CA with a family member with a history of heart disease and/or mental illness, who is concerned about developing osteoporosis, who has pondered over the utility of hormone replacement therapy, and who shops for organic foods and wants to put more fresh fruits and vegetables in her diet. That said, our readers should be interested in this post.

However, I am aware of the possibility that our readers have become attached to their multivitamins, having given up psychotropic drugs that they put high hopes in, but that turned to have more toxicity than therapy, or having flipped the bird at Sally Field and tossed their Boniva for osteoporosis prevention in the trash and turned to 'natural' vitamins and supplements instead. And since the *Drug Safety and Health News* has lost its advertising revenue from the pharmaceutical industry it is a bit going out on a limb to risk losing it from the makers of vitamins and supplements as well. But any way (deep breath) here goes...

The study is from data from the Women's Health Initiative, a large study conducted over many years on a range of health issues. The current article looked at 161,808 women with information collected on use of multivitamins over the course of eight years on average. There were no differences between women who did or did not take multivitamins in the risk of any type of cancer, heart attack or stroke. If anything, the risk of death was increased by 2%, which was not statistically significant. Additionally, a report from last month from the Physicians Health Study, which reported on 14,641 male physicians over the age of 50, did not find any effect on any type of cancer or total mortality or heart disease with supplementation with vitamins C or E over the course of ten years.[89]

I was watching public TV a couple of years ago when a researcher was being interviewed about the Beta Carotene and Retinol Efficacy Trial (CARET), in which 18,314 smokers took either beta carotene and Vitamin A or a placebo.[90] He embarrassedly stated that the beta carotene (found in carrots and orange vegetables) and Vitamin A, even though they are 'anti-oxidant' and theoretically should prevent heart disease and cancer, actually increased it in their trial. In fact, people on supplements equal to four carrots a day had 17% more heart disease and were 17% more likely to die than people on a placebo. People taking high doses of Vitamin A also doubled their risk of fracture,[91] leading Denmark to ban vitamin fortified Kellogg's breakfast cereals.[92] Alpha-Tocopherol, Beta Carotene (ATBC) Cancer Prevention Study smokers treated with beta-carotene and alpha tocopherol (Vitamin E) had an 8% increase in death,[93] while those with a prior history of heart attack had a 75% increase in heart attack with beta carotene therapy.[94] People on Vitamin E had a 2% increase in mortality. In all studies put together, there is an increased risk of heart disease with Vitamin A and beta carotene and no heart disease prevention with Vitamin E.[95] Vitamin A and beta carotene when taken together are associated with a 29% increase in mortality.[96] A study of Vitamin E combined with Vitamin C showed that vitamins actually accelerated the progression of thickening of the coronary arteries, and doubled the risk of dying of heart disease.[97] Another study of a combination of anti-oxidants, including Vitamins E, C, beta carotene, and selenium, showed that vitamins actually blocked the effects of anti-cholesterol treatment (simvastatin plus niacin) on reducing atherosclerosis and preventing heart attacks and strokes.[98] The vitamins in this study interfered with the ability of the other medications to raise HDL (good) cholesterol. Looking at all studies combined in which Vitamin E was given with beta carotene, there was a 10% overall increase in mortality. So, there it is (sigh).[99]

I found that pretty surprising, given all the hype you hear about the benefits of antioxidant vitamins.

I later visited my sister-in-law Rossana (pronounced ROE – SSSS – ana, as my kids always point out) in the US Virgin Islands. Rummaging in her refrigerator while she was at work (hey I didn't have anything else to do) I found several large bottles of vitamins and supplements. I looked at the ingredients and found that she was taking Vitamin A at several times the recommended daily levels. When she got home from work, I confronted her about it.

Doug: "Rossana, why are you taking so many vitamins and supplements?"

Rossana: "I don't have time to cook meals and eat enough vegetables, so this gives me what I need."

Doug: "But did you realize that the amount of Vitamin A you are taking may cause osteoporosis?"

[It's true-- women taking the highest amounts of Vitamin A supplements put themselves at risk for osteoporosis].

"Snap, crackle and pop, indeed!"

I don't want to be dodgy and name the company that made the vitamins and supplements she was taking, but I looked them up on the internet, and if you followed their recommendations, you would be spending $7,128 dollars per year on their products!

Even though in the laboratory there has been shown some connection between oxidative stress and heart disease, and in spite of the known role of vitamins C and E as anti-oxidants, you can't get around the fact that there is now a large body of research including studies with tens of thousands of patients that have shown that vitamins do not prevent heart disease or lengthen your life.

In fact, they may actually have the opposite effect.

I think the vitamins may be giving a boost to little tumors that wouldn't have been a problem otherwise.

I know the readers of this blog are going to protest and say they didn't use the right dose or right type of vitamins. But why don't you just get your vitamins from natural sources instead of a pill? And what about the conflicts of interest of those trying to sell you something? Here at *Drug Safety and Health News* we have been growing our own herbs and vegetables from seed. There is an added mental health benefit in helping the little parsley plants raise up their tired heads from the earth.

We can do it. Yes, we can!

My daughter always wanted to take a pill when she wasn't feeling well when she was a little girl, so my wife, after she had given her various cold remedies or whatever, would give her a pine nut. It was small, and tasty, and you could almost feel its beneficial effects.

For all you do, this (pine nut) pill is for you!

(Via Wikicommons By Burgkirsch, CC BY-SA 2.0 de)

Kind of like Obecalp, the fake medication sold to kids to make them feel better. See my post "Mommy Can I Have a Yummy Blue Pill?" Oh, btw Obecalp is placebo spelled backwards (I said that to make your head spin around like they did on the Exorcist).

Hat tip to Mrs. Bremner.

Now read online, "Herbs and Supplements for Weight Loss."[100]

[Update: I can fill in the name of the person behind the dodgy vitamin company, because in spite of his predictions that the products of Life Extension will make you live forever, Ray Kurzweil could very well be dead by the time this book is published.]

Chapter 39: Bogus Pimping for Flu Shots

(Originally posted February 12, 2009, in *Drug Safety & Health News Blog*).

In this week's *BMJ* there is an article by Thomas Jefferson of the Cochrane Vaccine Institute ("Relation of study quality, concordance, take home message, funding, and impact in studies of influenza vaccines: systematic review")[101] whom I have often quoted before (see "Flu Shots are for Idiots") regarding the dubious evidence behind policy recommendations regarding flu shots. Now he presents data that studies of flu shots funded by pharmaceutical companies are more likely to be published in prestigious journals than those funded by other sources, in spite of the fact that they have the same sample size and comparable methodology. He goes on to write:

> *The study shows that one of the levers for accessing prestige journals is the financial size of your sponsor. Pharmaceutical sponsors order many reprints of studies supporting their products, often with in-house translations into many languages. They will also purchase publicity space on the journal. Many publishers openly advertise these services on their website. It is time journals made a full disclosure of their sources of funding.*

A position supported by the staff at *Drug Safety and Health News*. He goes on to discuss the "impact factor", a metric related to how many times other authors of journal articles cite you in their articles, which is supposed to be a measure of how good or important your study is. However, there is a tendency to cite articles in the big journals like *JAMA* or *New England Journal of Medicine* just because we all think that if they got in there, they must be really good. What this does is give an advantage to those physicians and researchers who are doing the clinical trials funded by pharma, makes them more cited, enhancing their prestige, and hence even more valuable to their pharma friends. Soon everyone is wining and dining, have a good time, and making more money all around.

Yeah! Let's Have Some Drugs with our Wine!

But you can see how this has a corrupting influence on the practice of medicine. As pointed out in a letter to the editor of Houmatoday.com in Terrebonne Parish, Louisiana, by Dr. Randolph M. Howes ("Death by Peanut Butter or Drugs?"), 50% more people die of prescription drugs every hour than have collectively died from peanut butter.

Chapter 40: Taking Ecstasy No More Dangerous Than Riding a Horse?

(Originally posted February 15, 2009, in *Drug Safety & Health News*).

This just in from the European Desk of the *Drug Safety and Health News* blog, an article in the *Journal of Psychopharmacology* by Dr. David Nutt called "Equasy: An overlooked addiction with implications for the current debate on drug harms",[102] has been kicking up some dust in England.[103] Professor Nutt writes in this article that:

> *Drug harm can be equal to harms in other parts of life. There is not much difference between horse-riding and ecstasy.*

Hmmm. Dr. Nutt came up with the term "Equasy" to describe people who like to ride around on horses and then fall off and kill themselves or get brain damage. Apparently about 1/350 who ride horses regularly will do so. According to our English sources this article has been getting quite a bit of attention in the English press, and since he is head of the Advisory Council on Drugs Misuse this provoked a comment from the British Home Secretary.

> *I'm sure most people would simply not accept the link that he makes up in his article between horse riding and illegal drug taking.*

Indeed. But what if you got high and then went horse-back riding? And what about the movie *Equus*?

Anyhoo, I couldn't resist the photoshop opportunity to have Dr. Nutt go riding into the Sunset with our very own Lolcat, to fight these vicious English media people who are creating such a commotion.

We sel drugz to da reskew!

I read Dr. Nutt's paper and cannot argue with the data he presents that more people die in England from riding horses than taking Ecstasy. However, there is something creepy about comparing deaths from drug use and horseback riding. I mean horseback riding is a healthy and uplifting activity, while drug usage, even if it doesn't kill you, drags you down into lower levels of spiritual and mental functioning. On top of this Dr. Nutt was part of the shameful Advisory Board to Hoffmann-La Roche Pharmaceuticals at the Ritz Carlton in Alexandria, VA, in about 2002, where they paid them all several thousand dollars each to rubber stamp their report that Accutane (acne drug) could not cause depression (see "Are Dermatologists Dippy?"). Was I there? Nope.

Update: In this week's *BMJ* is a news piece about British Home Secretary requiring Dr. Nutt to apologize, and reactions from other doctors and politicians, as well as news that the Brits have decided to disregard Dr. Nutt's recommendation to downgrade the safety warnings for ecstasy.

Chapter 41: Republicans Try to Block Audacious Move to Inform Healthcare Treatments Based on the Evidence

(Originally posted February 16, 2009, in *Drug Safety & Health News*).

In a sign of their undying loyalty to drug and device makers the Republicans have declared their opposition to a plan to add a billion dollars to the stimulus package to study the relative cost and effectiveness of different treatments for chronic conditions, a plan which President Obama is expected to sign tomorrow. I simply had to ROTFL when I read this quote in the NY Times this morning ("US To Compare Medical Treatments"):[104]

> *Republican lawmakers and conservative commentators complained that the legislation would allow the federal government to intrude in a person's health care by enforcing clinical guidelines and treatment protocols.*

In other words, drug and device makers wouldn't be allowed to use expensive treatments that don't work! OMG!

The pharma and device maker cheerleaders don't have any rational reason for their retarded statements, so they get Rush Limbaugh to go on the air and blabber about how I don't want the government to tell me what kind of healthcare I got and here is a caller who lived in Canada and blah blah blah blah…

The article used several examples of bogus treatments that have not been shown to be better than conservative treatments, like surgery for neck pain, or claudication (pain in legs from artery disease). In fact, most of the examples involved bogus surgeries.

I hate surgeons!

As the article pointed out we now spend 16% of our gross domestic product (GDP) on healthcare, and that amount is expected to increase to 25% by 2025. The article quoted the CEO of Glaxo making a veiled reference to "other countries" who have tried to come up with rational guidelines to inform their clinical care. What he is referring to is the National Institute for Clinical Excellence (NICE) in England, where they actually evaluate what treatments do and do not work. I think the evaluations of treatments done by NICE are the best in the world. Needless to say, pharma doesn't like it when someone does a rational evidence-based assessment and comes to the conclusion that one of their drugs is useless, or no better than a cheaper generic.

Based on these guys logic, since it is a bad idea to find out if a treatment works or not, we might as well go back to the treatments of choice of the Middle Ages, like bloodletting.

Bloodletting, doctors' treatment of choice in 1780.

Pharmalittle comments on the topic are here[105] and comments from Howard Brody Hooked blog are here.[106]

Chapter 42: Philip Dawdy Should Be Excused for Smoking Because of his Mental Health Condition

(Originally posted February 16, 2009, in *Drug Safety & Health News*).

I was concerned to learn that Philip Dawdy, who writes on the *Furious Seasons* blog, was about to get kicked out of his apartment in Seattle. I grew up in Olympia WA and interviewed for a position in the Department of Psychiatry at the University of Washington in 2000 where I noticed that outside the University Hospital there was a sign that not only could you not smoke in the hospital, you couldn't smoke outside of the hospital, and in fact you had to move 200 yards AWAY from the hospital to smoke. I mean my wife is Italian born Italian and I am used to going to bars, restaurants, parties, etc., where everyone smokes. I think that this recent Seattle phenomenon is a sign of Eco-Fascism and as a psychiatrist I have to try and interpret what the root pathology might be. Hmmm... could it be an arrest at the oral stage of development ala Freud?

Anyhoo, rumors state that my sister, Anne Bremner, local Seattle lawyer and noted legal analysis commentator on CNN and FOX as well as lawyer for Amanda Knox in the Perugia Italy case, also a smoker, is getting similar harassments from Seattle Eco-Fascists, even though she owns her own property! We are going to have to get the half-cousins from Eastern Washington to come over there with their guns!

Anne Bremner

Rumors are that Anne might take on Philip's case pro bono! Do the Eco-fascists have a good legal basis for their actions? Only time will tell!

I felt so UPSET about this situation that I had to write a letter as a psychiatrist and physician scientist outlining my concerns, and here it is.

> *To whom it may concern,*
>
> *I am writing in regard to Philip Dawdy, a resident of your apartment complex. Mr. Dawdy has been diagnosed with bipolar disorder, a mental condition. Mr. Dawdy is currently addicted to nicotine in the form of smoking cigarettes. In my medical opinion, stopping the smoking of cigarettes may disrupt his mental condition in an unacceptable way, and it is therefore medically contraindicated for him to stop smoking cigarettes. Forcing him to either stop smoking cigarettes or to move out of his apartment is not in his best medical interest.*
>
> *Sincerely*
>
> *J. Douglas Bremner, M.D.*
>
> *Professor of Psychiatry and Radiology*

Atlanta, Georgia

Take this letter and use as you will, Philip.

Good Luck.

Dr. B.

[Note: the name of my university and the letter with my university's letterhead have been redacted at the request of the Dean of my university following a complaint from an outside source. It was pointed out to me by the Dean that use of my university's name and letterhead for personal use (which this was judged to be) was a violation of university policies. Also, people have taken this post to indicate that I am an advocate for smoking. I do not advocate smoking as it can cause heart disease and lung cancer. This blog is for entertainment purposes and is not to be taken as medical advice.]

[Update] I never found out who made this bullshit complaint, but it resulted in a letter being personally handed to me and an ongoing bizarre scenario where Emory University became "the university that cannot be named." Since all of the health care journalists were following my blog and using me as a source for their stories word quickly spread and the story got picked up by various news sources including *Inside Higher Ed,*[107] and my case got picked up by the Foundation for Individual Rights in Education (FIRE).[108] Eventually the lead science reporter for *The New York Times,* Gardiner Harris, wrote to the Dean asking why the chairman of my Department of Psychiatry could use Emory letterhead to write what amounted to a press release in support of the use of Paxil (paroxetine) in pregnancy while I was being punished for using Emory letterhead on my blog. I immediately got another hand-delivered letter stating that this had all been a misunderstanding. Now go read the book I wrote with my sister *Justice in the Age of Judgment: From Amanda Knox to Kyle Rittenhouse and the Battle for Due Process in the Digital Age* and[109] when you're done write a review on Amazon.com.

Chapter 43: No Vaccines for Me Please, But Thanks Anyway

(Originally posted February 17, 2009, in *Drug Safety & Health News*).

This week I had to fill out some online modules so that I could retain admitting privileges at Emory University Hospital in Atlanta, GA. Part of that involved filling out a questionnaire about vaccines where it asked if I had been immunized with the various vaccines for hepatitis, the flu, and chickenpox. Well, my daughter and I spent some quality time together with the chickenpox when she was three, so I don't need that vaccine, and the fact is that I never got vaccines for hepatitis, and I don't feel like getting one now. And readers of *Drug Safety and Health News* blog know my opinion about the influenza vaccine (see "Flu Shots Are for Idiots" in a previous volume in this series). The form included the lovely lie from the CDC about how 36,000 people die from the flu each year (half of those are actually flu-like illness, not the flu, get your facts straight, Julie). Anyhoo, they had a helpful multiple choice where they asked you *why* you weren't getting vaccinated, and for the flu I stated that they didn't work. After refusing the hepatitis vaccines the program froze me out, so when I went in to get my TB test, I asked the nurse about it, and she had me sign this declaration form about why I didn't want the vaccine. So, I decided to do some research. I found a Dr. Di Bisceglie touting the Hepatitis C vaccine in development, and what struck me was how LONG his list of disclosures were! Looky here:

> *Adrian M. Di Bisceglie, M.D., FACP, has disclosed that he has served on the advisory boards of Roche, Idenix, Novartis, Vertex, Bristol-Myers Squibb, Metabasis Therapeutics, Anadys, and Globe Immune. Dr. Di Bisceglie has also disclosed that he has received research support from Roche, Gilead Sciences, Idenix, Vertex, Bristol-Myers Squibb, and Sci-Clone. Dr. Di Bisceglie has also disclosed that he serves on the speaker's bureaus of Roche, Gilead Sciences, and Bristol-Myers Squibb. Dr. Di Bisceglie has also*

disclosed that he has served as a consultant to Bristol-Myers Squibb, Abbott, Schering Plough, Pharmasset, and Sci-Clone.

I mean geez, how can you do all that, plus do his research and be chairman of his department? Note that Roche is the maker of drugs for bird flu, which as I have written about in "Bird Flu Drugs are for Bird Brains" won't work once the virus mutates to spread to humans, but which has made a ton of money for them and their pitchman *ex* Vice President Cheney.

How to Poop on People

Anyhoo anyone who serves on eight advisory boards, gets research money from six companies, is on three speakers bureaus, and serves as a consultant to five companies, is spending an awful lot of time hob-knobbing and dining and getting payments and therefore is unlikely to be un-biased. For the hepatitis B vaccine there was some evidence that it might be associated with an increase in multiple sclerosis although it looks like the jury is still out on that one. As for Hepatitis C that is new, and we don't know the long-term risks. I don't get hepatitis vaccinations because even if you get it (which is unlikely) it probably won't kill you. Gardasil? As I have written before, I would rather have you guard your girls than give them Gardasil (see "Gardasil or Guard Your Girls? Or Guard Your Girls Against Gardasil?" in a previous volume).

Anyhoo here I am back filling out my infectious disease module.

As I was taking the online exam, I couldn't help but notice that it said that most Emory employees encountered potentially infectious materials in the workplace that could transmit HIV or Hepatitis through percutaneous transmission, i.e., needle sticks involving infected blood. However, they also listed "Other Potentially Infectious Material" (OPIM) as follows.

> ...semen, vaginal secretions, cerebrospinal fluid,
> synovial fluid, pleural fluid, pericardial fluid,
> peritoneal fluid, amniotic fluid, saliva in dental
> procedures, any body fluid that is visibly contaminated
> with blood, and all body ...

Did you notice the first few? It seemed odd that Emory Healthcare would be listing those as possible sources of transmission of viruses for people in the workplace! Especially for a place that is so worried about their public image, and which recently started a public "trust line" where people can call to anonymously report anything which is not consistent with Emory's morals and ethics, including conflicts of interest, apparently in response to recent negative publicity (but don't get me started on that). Anyhoo I was puzzling over this when I noticed the Emory logo...

Pills, Shills, and the Psychiatry Wars

Advancing the possibilities, indeed!

161

Chapter 44: A Brief History of Bastards

(Originally posted February 19, 2009, in *Drug Safety & Health News*).

Hmmm... Interesting title, you say. Yes indeed! Not every day you read about bastards in the Science Section of *The New York Times*. That, of course, is why readers have to come to alternative news sources like the *Drug Safety and Health News* blog to find information on more uncomfortable topics in the realm of medicine and mental health.

Anyhoo, the topic comes up because my beloved mother, who died when I was almost five years old, was adopted at birth, and a couple of years ago I had the adoption records opened and found out that she had been born out of wedlock.

Laurnell Bremner, in the year before she died.

I was able to track down some of her family, but others I wasn't sure if they wanted to know that their father had had a child (her) out of wedlock, but when the time came for us to have a belated memorial for her last fall, I decided that they should know about her. So, I called someone who was her half-sister, who didn't know about her, and the conversation went something like this:

ME: I am calling to let you know that you had a half-sister. She died in 1966. She was my mother.

HALF AUNT: How I am I supposed to believe you? [after receiving various pieces of information that I might be correct]. I am proud of you for your research. [awkward pause]

ME: Well, I don't want to butt into your life or anything, I just thought you should know.

HALF AUNT: I am proud of you for that as well. [awkward pause #2]

Click. I sent her a bunch of pictures and things about our wonderful families and all, with my phone number, but never heard back from her. Recently, I had another lost cousin contact me (yeah, the one from Eastern Washington with the guns and the stogies). I had tried to contact him earlier and thought maybe he didn't want to be found, but in fact he did. So, I thought I would contact the children of this woman, since maybe they wanted to know, and she shouldn't be the only keeper of family secrets. When I said that to another of my newly found cousins, she said I was being a bully and had "ambushed" the half-aunt. That was when I realized that half-aunt was actually ashamed of the fact that her half-sister was born out of wedlock. I had thought that such stigma against kids born out of wedlock was long gone, but maybe not. That got me to thinking, was Mommy a bastard? or was there another word for girls? That was why I was glad that one of my favorite things on the web, Yahoo! answers [a program that lets you ask a question and let a bunch of people answer, and then vote on the best answer], had asked "Can a female be a bastard?" had come back with the answer that she is a "bastard child." Not a bitch, that would be a female dog.

Phew!

Anyhoo I couldn't believe that people would still be prejudiced against people born out of wedlock. I mean we have an African-American president now for Christ's sake! Saying that half-aunt was born in the 30s and we should understand her views is like saying that we should go along with people who are racist against blacks cuz they were born in an earlier time!

BTW my genetic analysis showed that I am 4% black, and that is not "Black Norwegian" as the Bremners used to say about my Mom! That is Sub-saharan African!

Anyhoo all this reflection on bastards made me start reading about it. Turns out the term "illegitimate" refers to the fact that children born out of wedlock were literally not "legitimate", i.e., had no legal status as human beings, up until the laws were changed (in Britain at least) in the 1940s. Seems like the government was trying to punish people who had kids outside of marriage by depriving their kids of any legal right to exist. It was common practice to lie and say that the kid was actually the child of the grandparents (with the mother being the sibling) or the child of a second man, or any number of things. These kids were often put up for adoption (as was my Mom). They were also extremely vulnerable to abuse and neglect and were very insecure about themselves. Someone made the comment that it is morally dubious, at best, to blame the children for the actions of their parents.

The corporate staff at the *Drug Safety & Health News* couldn't agree more.

That is why we have declared the week of Feb. 2, 2009:

Be kind to a bastard week. :).

[Update] Ted Bundy was a bastard whose mother told him she was his sister and who was raised by his maternal grandparents. He attended the University of Puget Sound in Tacoma, Washington, where I went to school, as did my sister, Anne Bremner, and my father and uncle. Allegedly his father was his grandfather and the father of his mother, someone who used to swing cats around by the tail (where have I heard that before?). I wouldn't include him in our be kind to bastards week since he raped and killed multiple women. He was ultimately fried in the electric chair.

Chapter 45: More Bullshit Research About a Pill to Erase Bad Memories

(Originally posted February 20, 2009, in *Drug Safety & Health News*).

This week's issue of *Nature Neuroscience* has an <u>article</u> entitled "Beyond extinction: erasing human fear responses and preventing the return of fear."[110] Well if the title of the article wasn't enough to get your juices rolling I can tell you that they basically claim that they have discovered a pill that will erase traumatic memories and that could represent a miracle cure for posttraumatic stress disorder (PTSD). Needless to say, the journalist hoi poloi have had a field day over this one as they always do whenever they get a sniff of something that smells like a pill that can eliminate the misery of the human condition. The pill, of course, is propranolol, a beta blocker drug that blocks the norepinephrine beta receptors in the brain and has been noted to specifically block these receptors in a brain area called the amygdala, the seat of fear responses in the brain. Giving this drug in rats has been shown to interfere with the development of fear memories.

Most of the hype about propranolol's effects on fear and other emotions is based on research in rats, which leads me to ask the question, could it have been, perhaps, this particular rat?

This rat is pissed that his, well, humanity is not recognized.

He wouldn't have been the best cuz he would have had a, er, whadya call it, bad attitude? Having been the giant inflatable rat that made an appearance outside of Pfizer headquarters which led us to send the lolcats We Sel Drugz to the reskew.

Fast forward to humans and whether this drug can prevent the development of PTSD. Harvard psychiatrist Roger Pitman, M.D., did a study of propranolol in ER trauma victims and the data showed that it did not have a statistically significant effect on PTSD symptoms, although it did have an effect on heart rate and blood pressure responses.[111] This didn't stop the popular press from blowing their horns about this new magic pill that could be used to prevent PTSD. The next study by Vaiva et al also proposed that it demonstrated that propranolol prevented PTSD in acute trauma victims.[112] However this study did not use a randomized, placebo-controlled design. It showed that one patient out of 11 developed PTSD on propranolol versus 3/8 who "refused" propranolol in the ER. This is obviously a miniscule difference in a small group, factors that could influence who would "refuse" might affect treatment response, and obviously people who chose the active drug probably believed it would work, leading to a robust placebo response.

Enter the current study. In the background of studies that have been over hyped as preventing PTSD (when they don't) we now have a study showing that giving propranolol (a drug which lowers heart rate and blood pressure response) to normal people in the context of being re exposed to an upsetting film will result in lower heart rate and blood pressure response the next time they see the film.

And of course, their conclusion is that this has major implications for PTSD patients and other trauma survivors.

This is starting to solidify my belief that they shouldn't allow people from The Netherlands to do research. Oops! I take that back. Don't want to get cut out on my invitations to Amsterdam, har har har! (and it's NOT what YOU are thinking! Stop that!)

Let me cut through the bullshit here folks. Propranolol is not the magic bullet for the slings and arrows of outrageous fortune. All they did is show that if you can give a drug that hold down your blood pressure response to a traumatic film that the next time you see the film your blood pressure response will be lower. They also fail to cite the work of Larry Cahill. Who did a pretty similar experiment, as far as I can tell, ten years ago.[113]

You can't take a pill after a trauma or a grievous loss and make the pain go away.

Propranolol is not the magic pill. Get over it. You need psychotherapy to heal your hurting.

Now read online, "Can Changing Your Diet Help Your Depression?"[114]

Chapter 46: Henny Penny, the Sky Is Falling, and More News About Bird Flu Drugs

(Originally posted February 19, 2009, in *Drug Safety & Health News*).

In the news today (*USA Today*) is an article about the influenza virus which continues to quote the bogus statistics promulgated by the Centers for Disease Control (CDC) that 36,000 die every year from the flu (half of those are actually "flu-like illness" which is NOT the flu) and panders idiot advice that everyone should get the flu shot. What's new is that they point out the fact that the number of flu strains resistant to the bird flu drug Tamiflu (oseltamivir) is growing. It's not just that the makers of Tamiflu, Hoffmann-LaRoche, are my least favorite drug company, but that I have been predicting for over a year that if and when the bird flu became transmittable to humans, that Tamiflu would no longer be effective because the virus would have mutated (see "Bird Flu Drugs are for Bird Brains" if you don't believe me). The other anti-flu drug in this class is Relenza (zanamivir) which is taken in inhaled form.

The most widely prevalent strain of the flu this year, Type A H1N1, is resistant to Tamiflu. Type A H3N2 and Type B are not. H1N1 can be treated with Relenza if patients can tolerate the inhalation method. If not, they can take amantadine or rimantadine, but those drugs don't work against H3N2 flu or type B flu. Giving two drugs increases the side effects of nausea, nervousness and dizziness.

The actual bird flu, H5N1, was found last year to have been developing resistance to Tamiflu, as I had originally predicted, when it was reported that although previously less than 1% of influenza viruses were resistant to Tamiflu, that number increased to as many as 13%. The experts were quoted as saying that they were "surprised" that the virus could mutate to a form that is transmittable to humans and still be viable. However, as I had previously pointed out in "Bird Flu Drugs are for Bird Brains," if bird flu mutated to have human to human transmission, bird flu drugs probably wouldn't work anymore. But of course, that didn't stop the promotional machine from scaring the living daylights out of people and pumping up sales for Tamiflu.

Our former Chief Weasel in Charge of War Crimes Donald Rumsfeld personally made over a million dollars from the publicity through the stock he owns in the company that developed Tamiflu when the bird flu panic struck,[115] which he promulgated by holding press conferences to tell us that we were all about to die from the bird flu. Remember when, in response to the looting in Iraq a few years back, he said "Henny Penny the sky is falling!" Well, he probably said "Don't worry, Henny, your bird flu drug will protect you."

Here's a little virology 101. Bird flu is transmitted from birds to birds, not birds to humans. Actual human infections are pretty rare. And when and if it does mutate into a virus that can be transmitted to humans, the vaccine probably won't work anymore. What about for the regular flu? Tamiflu (and Zanamivir) are neuraminidase inhibitors; they prevent replication of influenza A and B viruses by interfering with the production and release of virus from cells that line the respiratory tract. They both need to be taken within 48 hours of the onset of flu symptoms to be useful. Although I say "useful" with tongue in cheek; if you get the flu, Tamiflu will reduce the number of days you have symptoms from about seven to about five.[116] Not a very big deal. And in terms of prevention, they cut your risk by about half. I don't want to take a drug all the time to prevent flu, do you? And if you take it after someone in your house gets sick, it's too late to prevent the flu.

Not only are drug companies trying get your money, gentle reader, it looks they want to drive you crazy as well. The Japanese drug regulatory agency has reported 64 cases of neuropsychiatric side effects, including "impaired consciousness, abnormal behaviors, hallucinations and other psychological and neurological symptoms" associated with Tamiflu, including two suicides.[117] There have also been reports of seizures. A spokesperson for the manufacturer of Tamiflu, however, denied that there was any association (they always say that—do you ever wonder if they have real people making these comments, or just some virtual online being or avatar or something programmed to say "we see no evidence of an association")?

[Update] Chat GPT, we've got another job for you!

Chapter 47: More Bad News About Bisphosphonates

(Originally posted February 21, 2009, in *Drug Safety & Health News*).

More bad news about bisphosphonate drugs for osteoporosis, which were bad enough to have readers write in about cases of erosive esophagitis and an incredible case of physician writing a case report, Jennifer Schneider, M.D., also a reader of this blog) about her own femoral fracture caused by getting out of her seat on a train while on alendronate (Fosamax). Well it looks like the medical community is starting to catch on as evidenced by a commentary in *JAMA* this week by Bridget Kuehn called "Long Term Risks of Bisphosphonates Probed" in which she highlights recent reports of increased risk of femoral fracture, atrial fibrillation, and esophageal cancer in women treated with bisphosphonate drugs like Fosamax and Boniva for osteoporosis, and points to the increasing awareness that treatment for longer than five years with these drugs probably worsens health outcomes.[118]

Sally Field, Chief Shill for osteoporosis drugs

A recent study by Lenart et al in 2009 showed that amongst a series of patients 37% of patients with subtrochanteric and femoral shaft fractures were on Fosamax (alendronate) compared to 11% of patients with hip or femoral neck fractures, indicating that long term treatment with this drug was associated with a specific type of fracture.[119] As I have previously written about, these drugs turn off bone turnover and after five years make bones more brittle, not less.

She also cited a letter to *The New England Journal of Medicine* by Diane Wysowski PhD of the FDA (old acquaintance from the Accutane wars) documenting 23 cases of esophageal cancer, with 8 deaths, in patients on bisphosphonates.

A terrible outcome of bisphosphonates of course is osteonecrosis of the jaw, which used to be called "Phossy jaw" cuz it was seen in match factory workers (the phosphorus in the matches got into the bone and turned off bone turnover), a condition so terrible it drove match factory workers to suicide. Nowadays we call it "Fossy jaw" in honor of our old friend, Fosamax (see "Ladies Don't Get Sucked Into the Bone Mineral Density Testing Rat Maze").

Now read online, "Should I Get My Bone Mineral Density (BMD) Checked?"[120]

Chapter 48: Sex, Drugs, and Seroquel

(Originally posted February 25, 2009, in *Drug Safety & Health News*).

Kudos to Philip Dawdy at the *Furious Seasons* blog for his original reporting on the litigation behind the antipsychotic drug Seroquel (quetiapine). Thousands of people have brought lawsuits against the maker of Seroquel, AstraZeneca, because the drug was pushed off label for the treatment of conditions other than schizophrenia and bipolar disorder, the conditions it was approved for, without adequate warning that the drug could cause weight gain, which leads to heart disease and diabetes. Not too good for a drug that is associated with only a 10% improvement in depression, while it increases the risk of life threatening diabetes, and is associated with a 25% increase in sedation, based on studies in the *American Journal of Psychiatry*[121] and *Journal of Clinical Psychopharmacology*.[122]

Now it comes out that Dr. Wayne MacFadden, who was heading up the group that was performing clinical trials of Seroquel for bipolar, was banging: 1) one of the study investigators; 2) a ghost writer writing manuscripts and preparing posters and presentations about the drug; 3) two other research assistants and/or employees. He also offered sexual favors in return for getting inside scoops from the investigator about other competing drug companies and tried to intimidate her about reading the literature related to other drug trials. I wonder if he was one of the early members of the ACNP who according to (ill founded, I'm sure) rumor opted to have their annual meeting in Puerto Rico cuz they had cheaper whores? (see "A Dissenting Opinion on Antidepressants from the ACNP"). And in the end, it looks like after all that aggravation, the investigator in question who was identified as a doctor at the Institute of Psychiatry in London, apparently didn't even get her name on the friggin paper!

I've been through THAT aggravation!

The funniest part is that Philip emailed the Editors of *The American Journal of Psychiatry* where one of the studies, with the cheesy name of "Bolder" was published, asking for a comment about whether this affected their opinion of the integrity of the trial results, and one of them responded "Let's not respond to this guy anymore." But then copied Philip on the email! HA HA!

Sometimes these older generation guys are a little clueless on basic use of the computer. So let us digress now for a little lesson. When you get an email and want to respond to it, there are two choices: reply and reply all.

Don't hit the button on the right, unless you are absolutely sure.

More on this story here.[123]

Chapter 49: Confessions of a Former PsychNetter

(Originally posted March 3, 2009, in *Drug Safety & Health News*).

Senator Charles Grassley, up to his usual mischief, has released a brochure from a GlaxoSmithKline program called "PsychNet", which was developed in 2000 in order to promote sales of their antidepressant Paxil (paroxetine). PsychNet involved getting a bunch of influential psychiatrists together and training them to go out and give talks to other psychiatrists. Here are the program objectives:

- *Develop and/or solidify relationships with key influential psychiatrists and primary care physicians.*
- *Develop these physicians into knowledgeable and engaging speakers on Paxil and its effective treatment on mood and anxiety disorders.*
- *Build advocacy amongst PsychNet physicians by creating speaking opportunities.*

This is an internal document and shows what industry is thinking about psychiatry "key opinion leaders" (KOLS). Those are the influential physician guys. I think the choice of language is illuminating: "build advocacy" by "creating speaking opportunities"? In other words, set up high paying speaking gigs for the big boys, not cuz you are good guys who want to educate, but to provide a way to transmit money (and therefore good will and influence) with those leaders who will in turn influence the little guys to prescribe your drug.

That is actually a violation of federal anti-kickback laws as far as I can tell. The Justice Department is actually using this law now to prosecute Forest labs for illegal promotion of off label use of the antidepressants Celexa and Lexapro for teenagers (for whom they do not work and can be harmful). Here are some quotes from today's NY Times[124]:

> *"Somehow physicians think they're different from the rest of us," Mr. Morris said. "But money works on them just like everybody else."*

Mr. Sullivan, the United States attorney, said officials hoped to send a strong message to doctors. "I have been shocked at what appears to be willful blindness by folks in the physician community to the criminal conduct that corrupts the patient-physician relationship," he said.

Anyway, the PsychNet Program goes on to state that:

> *PsychNet is an ideal way for key opinion leaders to influence clinicians in your region on the benefits of Paxil versus competitors.*

> *PsychNet Speakers – Selection and training*

> *Each region selected several physicians who are influential in their communities, credible and interested in speaking on behalf of Paxil. Specifically, the physicians met the following criteria:*

> *Local key opinion leaders*

> - *Educated on the benefits of Paxil.*
> - *Strong communication skills*
> - *A list of regional speakers can be found at the back of this booklet.*

I am not making this up, guys. The program goes on to say that only doctors that had gone through the program could give talks, because they were "educated" on the advantages of Paxil over competing drugs for depression and anxiety.

Those guys know that physicians look up to their KOLs, first during training, then later to get updates on what is new. That is why it is so concerning when they get co-opted by drug companies, which is what has happened in the US today.

"I wanna be like you when I grow up!"

That's our dog, Lydia, who tragically met her demise five years ago.

I actually gave a talk for a program like this somewhere around 2001 in Orlando, FL. Right before I went out to give my talk one of the industry guys said:

Go out there and sell some Paxil, Doug!

That was when I started to realize that something was terribly wrong.

My kids got to go to Disneyworld, though. First and last time.

Bremner kids have fun while Dad sells drugs.

That's a real picture. No kidding.

Anyhoo, after the Disneyworld show I had a gig for a year speaking in a program called "What Does Neurobiology Tell Us?" Well, what it told us obviously was that we should be prescribing antidepressants, of course! I used to try and change the slide cuz I thought it was doing a paid infomercial to use only their slides but present myself as coming from Emory University (and not the drug company). They said they couldn't do that cuz the slides were "FDA approved" (?). Go figure. So, I would show up and switch the slides at the last minute. At the end of the year, they dropped me.

In retrospect it would have been a lot easier to just go along with the program and not fight them.

Relax and have some wine with your drugs! And some cash!

But then I wouldn't get to play with lolcats!

WE HAZ GOOD TIMZ HEAR AT DRUG NEWZ BLOG!

The next generation of young doctors seems to be putting up a fight against pharma corruption.[125] But we all know about the ideals of youth.

Nevertheless, consider this an open invitation to the American Medical Students Association in the fight to withstand influence; I am willing to help in any way I can. Just let me know.

See more responses to the PsychNet brochure here.[126]

[Update: Looking back on this, I realize I said I was part of a program "like" the PsychNet program. As I remember it, the meeting in Orlando *was* part of the PsychNet program. So, although I admit I was part of it in the title, I kind of weasel around it in the text. I don't know why I did that, maybe I thought Senator Grassley would put me in jail. The main force behind things like the Sunshine Act, which forced physicians to disclose the payments they received from drug companies, was not Senator Grassley, of course, but his aid, Paul

Thacker. Gardiner Harris, a reporter for *The New York Times,* also played a major role in causing a sea change in how things were done. I do remember feeling ashamed of the association with PsychNet and GSK, but the corrosive way these things unfold, you find yourself a part of them before you even realize what is going on. After I wrote *Before You Take that Pill: Why the Drug Industry May be Bad for your Health* there was never any further question about whether I would be participating in PsychNet or any of the other pharmaceutical industry reindeer games.]

Chapter 50: More Evidence That Drug Companies Pack More Punch Than the Rest of Us

(Originally posted March 4, 2009, in *Drug Safety & Health News*).

I got a little pissed the other day when I read that the editors of *The American Journal of Psychiatry* had said "let's not respond to this guy" when Philip Dawdy asked them if they should re-consider the data from the BOLDER trial of Seroquel in bipolar depression, which has been tainted by allegations of sexual affairs between study investigators (see "Sex, Drugs and Seroquel"). Well I thank Hoffmann-La Roche Pharmaceuticals and my dispute with them about whether their acne drug Accutane can cause depression for: 1) deposing me 16 times; 2) calling me a liar); 3) attacking my professional reputation; 4) suing my university; 5) trying to get me fired from my university; 6) trying to get my paper on the effects of Accutane on the brain retracted; 7) accusing me of fraud to the Editor (yes, Robert Freedman M.D.) of the journal where the paper was published, which led to, 8) more inquiries at my university.

I guess it is confirmation on a personal level of the results of a recent study showing that studies funded by pharmaceutical companies were more likely to get published in prestigious journals than the others, even after controlling for study results and quality. The authors concluded that the big journals behavior was possibly (?) influenced by ad revenues related to drugs (see "Bogus Pimping for Flu Shots").

Well, when a multi-billion-dollar drug company showed up at Dr. Freedman's door he certainly didn't ignore them but sent the following very intimidating letter me and the Dean of the Emory School of Medicine (i.e., my employer).

The American Journal of Psychiatry

1000 Wilson Boulevard, Suite 1825
Arlington, VA 22209-3901
Telephone 703.907.8640
Fax 703.907.1096
E-mail ajp@psych.org

December 19, 2007

To: Thomas J. Lawley, M.D.
    J. Douglas Bremner, M.D.

Fr: Robert Freedman, M.D.
    Michael D. Roy

cc: Joann MacBeth, J.D., Crowell & Moring

Enclosed is a letter that accompanied a box of materials we received from Colleen M. Hennessey at Peabody & Arnold, LLP, the firm representing Hoffman La Roche in the trial at which an article published in the May 2005 issue of The American Journal of Psychiatry was called into question.

In the letter they point to specific points brought up in testimony that suggests the Journal should conduct an investigation.

Since we have already requested that an inquiry be conducted with regard to this study, we are forwarding the letter to ensure that the results of the investigation have addressed these points.

We had previously sent you the court transcript of the judge's decision that first prompted our request for the inquiry. Throughout the letter, Ms. Hennessey refers to sections of the court transcripts of the hearings. These were enclosed in the box of materials sent to our offices. Since the proceedings cover 9 court sessions over 5 days of testimony, we are now in possession of over 1,300 pages.

We are logistically unable to copy all of these pages and send to each of you, so if there is one specific designee to whom these materials should be sent, please forward the name and mailing address of that individual to Michael Roy (mroy@psych.org).

The American Journal of Psychiatry

1000 Wilson Boulevard, Suite 1825
Arlington, VA 22209-2901
Telephone 703.907.8680
Fax 703.907.1096
E-mail ajp@psych.org

We note that Dr. Bremner has already retracted a study published in *Biological Psychiatry*. If your inquiry finds serious errors or omissions in this study, we also request that your inquiry verify the other studies published in *The American Journal of Psychiatry* from Emory University.

Editor-in-Chief
Robert Freedman, M.D.

Deputy Editors
David A. Lewis, M.D.
Robert Michels, M.D.
Daniel S. Pine, M.D.
Susan K. Schultz, M.D.
Carol A. Tamminga, M.D.

Editorial Director
Michael D. Roy

Senior Editor/Features Writer
Jane Weaver, E.L.S.

Senior Editors
John J. Guardiano, Ph.D.
Leannah M. Harding, M.S., E.L.S.

Assistant Editors
Lisa Devine
Angela Moore

Production Editor
Julie C. Blair

Senior Graphic Designer
Jason Glanos

Editorial Manager
Molly Douglas

Editorial Assistant
Samantha Luck

Administrative Assistant
Kourtney Skinner

We very much appreciate your cooperation in this matter.

Sincerely,

Robert Freedman, M.D.
Editor in Chief

Michael D. Roy
Managing Editor

1. Bremner JD, Fani N, Ashraf A, Votaw JR, Brummer ME, Cummins T, Vaccarino V, Goodman MM, Reed L, Siddiq S, Nemeroff CB: Functional brain imaging alterations in acne patients treated with isoretinoin. American Journal of Psychiatry 2005; 162:983-991.

Enclosures:

1. Original article in *The American Journal of Psychiatry* by Bremner et al.

2. Judge Francine A Schott's Ruling, November 8, 2007

3. List of publications in *The American Journal of Psychiatry* by Dr. Bremner

4. Notice of Retraction from *Biological Psychiatry*

cc: J. Douglas Bremner, M.D.

Wouldn't you be bummed to get a letter like this? I sure as hell was. All I can say is don't get in the way of Big Pharma.

They also enclosed a list of 19 articles I had authored in their journal and based on this bogus fraud accusation from a drug company they wanted Emory to look at ALL the studies I had ever published! For the past 20 years!

I used to think that I would get some respect as a Professor of Psychiatry and Radiology. Not anymore. Those guys are a bunch of meanies, and they don't care what you, I, or the bedpost think. Don't get in between them and their profits.

My crime? Doing a brain imaging study that showed their drug for pimples could affect the brain, and therefore cause depression. Rather than discuss the evidence from a broad range of clinical and animal research that their drug (which the body actually produces naturally, which most people don't know) could affect behavior, they decided to trash me instead, spending hundreds of thousands of dollars to hire an expert to go through and pick apart everything they could about my study.

Makes you wonder how they get to sleep at night.

Oh btw Dr. Freedman I did not "retract" any study. I wrote a paper when I was at Yale that we found out had an error in part of the data and there was a dispute about what to do about it. When Roche found out about the dispute their lawyers high tailed it up there to depose the authors to see if they could dig up some dirt. That actually worked out OK for me cuz they subpoenaed all the emails which included this one between the two dissenting authors the day before a conference call amongst the authors to decide what to do about the paper. They wrote:

Let's have some fun with Doug tomorrow.

Why didn't you just say so! If you want to have fun with Doug, have I got just the one for you!

LEZ HAV SUM FUN WITH DUG!

I mean after all, who doesn't like to have fun? Anyhoo these guys wrote a letter to the journal, *Biological Psychiatry*, saying that they thought the article should be retracted, and that not to do so would be "defamation", while simultaneously turning around and accusing me of fraud at Emory University, which led to an inquiry, which found the charges to be not founded. The journal meanwhile retracted the article "based on legal counsel and for legal reasons" which probably means they were threatened with a lawsuit. The data (the correct part) was published in a later paper.[127]

As for the article on the effects of Accutane on the brain,[128] Roche hired a well-known radiologist-researcher who threw out so many red herrings about complicated research details and methods that it got everyone confused. And four years later all this sturm und draum led to the finally, relatively minor, correction.[129] Only 7 subjects in each treatment group completed the Skindex post-treatment. The secondary analysis that included whole brain metabolism before and after treatment did not reach significance on re-analysis."

In other words, after wasting several million dollars and everyone's time the basic conclusion that Accutane (isotretinoin) affects brain function was unchanged. The data even looked a little better than before on re-analysis.

Thanks guys! Look forward to working with you again!

I'll leave you with a final quote from Hoffmann-La Roche Pharmaceuticals (in the context of why they charge $18,000 per year for an HIV drug in Korea where hardly anyone makes that much, total, in a single year, so they can't afford the drug.

We are not in the business of saving lives. We are in the business of making money. Our business is making money.

Good job guys!

Chapter 51: We Won! Supreme Court Overrules Preemption

(Originally posted March 5, 2009, in *Drug Safety & Health News*).

"Congress did not intend FDA oversight to be the exclusive means of ensuring drug safety and effectiveness" – Justice John Paul Stevens

Wyeth, Drugmakers Lose as Top U.S. Court Allows Suits (Update1)

By Greg Stohr

March 4 (Bloomberg) — The U.S. Supreme Court bolstered patient lawsuits against drugmakers, upholding a $7 million award to a woman who lost her arm after being injected with Wyeth's Phenergan nausea treatment.

The justices, voting 6-3, said patients can use state product-liability laws to accuse companies of failing to provide adequate safety warnings. Drugmakers had argued that they were shielded from suit by the Food and Drug Administration's approval of a treatment and its packaging information.

Thanks to those of you who joined the Stop Preemption cause on FB which grew to 166 members.

Read my prior pieces on preemption including "Corporations Get a Get Out of Jail Free Card" and "No Redemption for Preemption."

One of our readers, Sara Bostock, filed a friend of the court brief on behalf of Levine (i.e., anti preemption). Note the reporting is very biased toward the pro-preemption side.

Chapter 52: Edward Munch and Live Blogging from the American Psychosomatic Society Meeting in Chicago

(Originally posted March 5, 2009, in *Drug Safety & Health News*).

Mrs. Bremner and I played hooky from the American Psychosomatic Society (APS) Meeting on Friday to visit the Chicago Institute of Art, where they had an exhibition on the artist Edvard Munch, which was a real *scream*. That is one of the perks of our travel intensive lifestyle, is getting to visit art galleries in other cities. Most of us have only seen the painting "The Scream", which was recently stolen (and then returned) from a museum in Oslo, Norway (sorry! won't do it again). However, he has a number of wonderful paintings. Here is his self-portrait.

Didn't anyone tell you that smoking is bad for you, Edvard?

And I was particularly interested to learn that, like me, his mother died when he was five years old, and also like me, he had occasional bouts of anxiety.

Not a good feeling.

His paintings really strike a chord, though, described by a contemporary critic as:

> *A breath of fresh air from unseen worlds.*

Or something like that. He focused on themes like love and death that speak to us all, like this one:

Grief, the eternal condition.

Many of us spend our entire lives grieving, if we are lucky enough to even get to the starting line. Grief, or what is worse not even getting to the point where you can start to grieve, is the cause of much mental health problems today.

In Sicily, where Mrs. Bremner comes from, the women traditionally wore black for a year when someone died. So, when you went to the villages in the interior, all of the women were wearing black, cuz someone had always died.

If they were outside, that is (most of the time all day indoors making pasta).

I think the US has something to learn from them. I love cemeteries.

My mom's headstone.

Yes, I cry when I see these pictures. But at least I can cry. That is more than I could have said for most of my life.

And that is your mental health Alt CME for the day, boys and girls.

It is interesting how Munch has been interpreted. Called a "neurasthenic" in his day, a psychiatric diagnosis (no longer used) which describes anxiety, depression, psychosomatic concerns, he actually promoted this as a way to market himself as an "alternative artist", although it is clear he suffered mental torments. A friend and fellow Bohemian Berlin Cafe sitter, a Polish man named Przybyszewski wrote critiques of his art highlighting the misogynist nature of Munch. He is in this painting in the foreground.

Przybyszewski.

He even changed titles of his painting showing a woman kissing a man's neck to "Vampire" from "Love and Pain." Munch was a good one on love though. Check this one out:

Madonna

Classic femme fatale. Just like Mrs. Bremner!

I was interested to learn that Munch, like many artists, did not care about the titles of his paintings, and so they were made by dealers or people like his Polish friend. That guy later killed his wife and abandoned his children. Not a very good one to learn about the meaning of Munch's paintings. I think Munch was expressing the unconscious mind, and the "meaning" of his paintings didn't really matter.

Kinda like the content of the *Drug Safety and Health News* blog.

Oops! This is supposed to be science. I take that back.

Chapter 53: Statins Interfere with Orgasms: Live Update from APS in Chicago

(Originally posted March 6, 2009, in *Drug Safety & Health News Blog*).

Mrs. Bremner and I are at the American Psychosomatic Society (APS) Annual Meeting in Chicago this week where the most interesting presentation other than our poster and talk on brain and heart mechanisms mediating the increased risk for mortality in people with heart disease and depression, is this late breaking data showing that statins have a negative effect on orgasms.

In "Statins Reduce Orgasm: Results from the UCSD Statins Study" Dr. Beatrice Golomb and colleagues from the University of California-San Diego reported today on their 1,067 men and women without heart disease with a LDL cholesterol of 119-190 mg/dL who were randomized to either pravastatin (Pravachol), simvastatin (Zocor), or placebo for LDL cholesterol reduction with the purpose of prevention of heart attacks. Orgasm was self-rated on a scale of 1 ("much worse") to 5 ("much better") with 3 for "no change." Overall statins had a negative effect on orgasms, with a reduction of 0.63 for men and 0.57 for women, which was statistically significant only for men, and only for Zocor.

Previous studies have shown that the more you reduce LDL cholesterol the more you lower your risk of heart attack. It has also been shown that you increase your risk of cancer more, and now this study shows that the more LDL cholesterol goes down the more it messes up your orgasm. So, we have a drug that doesn't reduce overall mortality in men without heart disease (as in the current study) (see "Zetia, Schmetia") and has no beneficial effect at all for women without heart disease, and that increases risk of cancer, that not only makes you stupid, but that messes up your orgasm.

Dr. Golomb's quote to *USA Today* about the study was that:

> *It takes a lot of energy to have an orgasm.*

Nice quote, Beatrice. She says that statins can interfere with Coenzyme Q and do other things that may impair energy utilization.

Mrs. Bremner's comment on the study is that they probably thought that statins would improve orgasms through their anti-inflammatory effect.

Today I am listening to presentations (and writing as I listen) from the Study of Women's Health in the US (SWAN) study on women in mid-life, we learn that Chinese women have less osteoporotic fractures (7 year incidence of 4.8) than black (4.5) and Caucasian women (8.1), however mid-life women in general feel that they are wiser and have a stronger sense of purpose than they did in their younger life, and that going through menopause is associated with a temporary increase in hot flashes and forgetfulness, but no significant increase in depression. Also, the Mid Life in the US (MIDUS). National Study, which was funded by the MacArthur Foundation, asked the question, what is wellbeing? And what effect does it have on people throughout the lifespan. Aristotle defined wellbeing, or "eudaimonia", thus:

> The highest of all human goods is realization of human potential.

In the MIDUS study, autonomy, personal growth, feelings of purpose in life, positive relations with other, environmental mastery, and self-acceptance, increased over time for people in mid-life or did not change for people 55-74, while they didn't improve or went down for those younger or older than this group. These qualities were also associated with better health outcomes. They also predicted lower lipid levels, better metabolism, and other goodies.

Next read online, "Herbs and Supplements for Menopausal Symptoms."[130]

Chapter 54: Should I Take an Aspirin or Put a Gun to My Head

(Originally posted March 9, 2009, in *Drug Safety & Health News Blog*).

A recent report from the US Preventive Services Task Force (USPSTF) shows that daily aspirin in people without a history of heart disease will prevent heart attacks in men, and strokes in women. In both groups the benefit of heart attack or stroke prevention needs to be weighed against the risk of gastrointestinal bleeding. The guidelines state that men over 45 and women over 55 should take a daily aspirin. And that no one over 80 should take aspirin. The investigators concluded that aspirin doses of greater than 100 mg per day (i.e., more than baby aspirin) did not add additional benefit.

An analysis of the published literature of people without heart disease examined a total of 51,342 women and 44,114 men from a range of studies who did not heart disease but had risk factors for heart disease.[131] Daily aspirin in women reduced cardiovascular disease by 12%, which was statistically significant, with a 17% reduction in stroke and no effect on heart attacks or cardiovascular mortality. However, for any given woman, the absolute risk reduction, or how much the risk of heart attack was reduced in that individual, was only 0.3% over a six-year period. And aspirin increased the risk of major bleeding by 68%. For men there was a 14% reduction of cardiovascular events primarily related to a 32% reduction in heart attacks with no effect on strokes or cardiovascular mortality. That translated into a .37% absolute reduction over a six-year period. And men had a 72% increase in major bleeding. Aspirin did not save any lives in men or women. And as pointed out by Mrs. Bremner for every stroke in women or heart attack in men that is prevented by aspirin, there is one major gastrointestinal bleeding event caused by aspirin.

For men with a history of heart disease, taking baby aspirin every day can reduce your risk of death from heart disease by about 17% (ATC 2002).[132] Translated, this means you are reducing your risk by about 1% per year. Although technically the risk of stomach bleeding is outweighed by the heart benefits of aspirin (which can only be shown when large numbers of patients are studied), in terms of what that means to you the differences are clinically meaningless.

In patients with strokes or transient ischemic attacks (TIAs) aspirin plus dipyridamole (a blood vessel dilator) was shown to be associated with a 13% rate of cardiovascular event compared to 16% on aspirin alone, a difference that was statistically significant.[133]

Overall, I think aspirin for disease prevention is a bunch of hooey invented by cardiologists. My father almost died from bleeding from taking aspirin for such a purpose.

A friend of mine used the aspirin story to illustrate how incredibly weak some clinical trial data really was.

Hat tip to CDC Mole.

Now read online, "Do I Have an Ulcer or is it Just Gastroesophageal Reflux Disease (GERD)?"[134]

Chapter 55: Use these Drugz Cuz I Said So

(Originally posted March 11, 2009, in *Drug Safety & Health News Blog*).

This week's *JAMA* has an article that evaluates guidelines written for the appropriate treatment of a variety of cardiac conditions.[135] These are guidelines written by experts in the field about appropriate treatments for a variety of conditions, from heart attacks to atrial fibrillation. The guidelines were ranked according to level of evidence, with guidelines ranked as A being based on multiple clinical trials, B based on a single study, and C based on expert opinion, "standard of care", or case studies. The study showed that in 54% of cases, the guidelines were based on evidence ranked as C, in other words the personal opinions of whoever was writing the guidelines. The other finding was that the number of guidelines were increasing all the time, in spite of the fact that the evidence to support these opinions wasn't.

In other words, about half the time someone is writing something and everyone else is supposed to go along. This is actually how medical education works; you see the professor prescribe in a certain way, and you do the same. Given the fact that the pharmaceutical industry has moved in and gotten control of leaders in their fields, through payments for consulting and lecturing, whom they derisively refer to as "KOLs" (Key Opinion Leaders), and whom pay consulting groups to "manage their KOLs", you shouldn't have much confidence in these guidelines, as I wrote about recently in "How Much You Gonna Pay Me for Those Guidelines."

2/19/05

DR. CURT FURBERG
Wake Forest University
Public Health Services Dept.

C-SPAN 2

"The [company] reps tell the doctors, 'You should follow these guidelines,' implying that you're not a good doctor if you don't follow these guidelines."

Dr Curt Furberg testifies before Congress regarding expert consensus guidelines.

Hey! I think I came up with a better use for those guidelines!

A better use for expert consensus guidelines.

Chapter 56: Don't Squeeze the Sharma

(Originally posted March 14, 2009, in *Drug Safety & Health News Blog*).

I recently became aware of a psychiatrist from the Institute of Psychiatry at King's College in London named Tonmoy Sharma, M.D., once a prominent academic psychiatrist in England with multiple papers and books who appeared frequently on the BBC. He made hundreds of thousands of dollars in outside consulting and speaking work for drug companies over the past decade or so.

Tonmoy Sharma, M.D.

Charges of ethical lapses were brought against him for his conduct in industry sponsored drug trials of psychiatric patients, and although he countered with various defamation lawsuits and the like, he was finally found to be responsible for conducting research without appropriate human subjects approvals, improperly presenting himself as having a PhD, and selling drugs he got for free from drug companies for his research to hospitals. Someone described him as being only interested in making money. Finally, after eight years, he was stripped of his license by the British General Medical Council.[136]

> *Andrew Popat, chairman of the panel, told Sharma:*
> *"Your persistent and wide-ranging dishonesty and*
> *untruthfulness, spanning a number of years, together*
> *with your lack of insight, is so serious that it is*

> *fundamentally incompatible with your continuing to be*
> *a registered medical practitioner."*

He failed to appear at a hearing for accusations against him of fraud and skipped the country; now he is purported to be a fugitive in the US.

It took a while (eight years) and a lot of lawyer time and defamation lawsuits before this happened though. That is why I say if you don't have some stamina.

Don't squeeze the Sharma.

Where have you been lately, Mr. Whipple?

That is not the only "action" going on at the Institute of London.

As I have written about here previously (see "Sex, Drugs and Seroquel"), and as chronicled by Philip Dawdy on his blog *Furious Seasons*, the leader of the "BOLDER" studies of Seroquel (quetiapine) for the treatment of bipolar disorder, Wayne MacFadden M.D., was disclosed to be having an affair with an academic psychiatrist at the Institute of Psychiatry in London who was a study investigator in trials of Seroquel from 2000-2006, during which time he emailed her about offering sexual favors for news about competing drug companies and other things. These shenanigans raised questions about the integrity of the findings from the BOLDER studies, which were used for the basis of FDA approval for Seroquel for bipolar depression. The fact that AstraZeneca instructed its employees to lie to doctors and tell them that there was no evidence that Seroquel could cause diabetes, when there was evidence to the contrary, is further cause for concern. When Philip Dawdy wrote to *The American*

Journal of Psychiatry editors, including Robert Freedman, M.D., asking if they would reexamine the BOLDER study published in their journal, they ignored him, but inadvertently replied, "I don't think we should respond to this guy." A published letter to the *Journal of Clinical Psychiatry* about the other BOLDER study by Philip asking why they didn't do a last observation carried forward analysis was rebuffed by the authors as not being needed and "statisticians don't favor that analysis anymore."

Oh, really?

I have written before about use of atypical antipsychotics (Seroquel, Abilify, Risperdal, Zyprexa) for non-psychotic depression and the fact is they are more likely to cause akathisia than cure the blues, and they can also cause life threatening diabetes. It is a tragedy how these drugs have been foisted on the American public, and I think people are getting sick of it and fighting back. I saw to my fellow physicians it is time to take our profession back.

[Update] Tonmoy Sharma migrated to the United States and opened a series of drug treatment facilities in California, where apparently the regulatory authorities did not read my blog. He was recently the subject of an FBI raid.

Chapter 57: They're Dropping Like Flies on their SSRIs

(Originally posted March 16, 2009, in *Drug News & Health News*).

Well, maybe not really, but you might think so if you read about this recent study[137] and accompanying editorial[138] in the *Journal of the American College of Cardiology* that is hot off the press (thanks to Marilyn Mann who is an ACC member for getting the paper for guys like us to review, when the paper isn't even out yet even though they are blowing the press releases all over the mainstream media).

This study looked at 63,469 women in the Nurses' Health Study who didn't have a history of heart disease, divided them into different levels of depression based on the self-report Mental Health Inventory, and then followed them over several years. They found the usual associations between depression and risk of heart attack, but what was more interesting was the fact that women on antidepressants were three times as likely to have a sudden cardiac death than women not on antidepressants. This was pretty striking and was not accounted for by other factors such as risk factors for heart disease. Granted, sudden cardiac death in healthy women is fairly rare, and in this study only 46/100,000 women on an SSRI had a sudden cardiac death.

Tricyclics have long been known to prolong the cardiac Q-T interval, so they could theoretically cause ventricular arrhythmia, leading to sudden death. The SSRIs have been promoted as being safer from this standpoint, however in the current study there were not any differences between Selective Serotonin Reuptake Inhibitors (SSRIs) and "other antidepressants" in terms of sudden cardiac death.

The graph below shows the risk of sudden cardiac death over time. It is called a "survival curve" and shows what percentage of the women had died up to that point of time. The women who were most depressed and on antidepressants are the blue line; they were most likely to die. Behind them are nondepressed women on antidepressants, and women not on antidepressants.

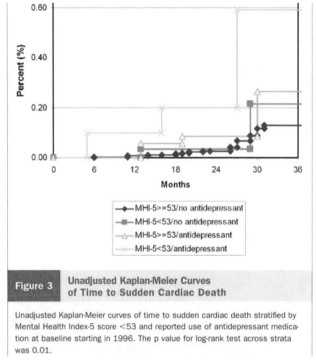

Figure 3	Unadjusted Kaplan-Meier Curves of Time to Sudden Cardiac Death

Unadjusted Kaplan-Meier curves of time to sudden cardiac death stratified by Mental Health Index-5 score <53 and reported use of antidepressant medication at baseline starting in 1996. The p value for log-rank test across strata was 0.01.

We are climbing... Jacob's ladder...

Mrs. Bremner's comment is that sudden cardiac events is fairly rare in otherwise healthy women, and antidepressants did not increase the risk of other cardiac events that are more common, like heart attack and stroke. Nevertheless, she thinks it is worth paying attention to.

Chapter 58: LOLCats Invite Obama to Dance in Honor of Whistleblowers

(Originally posted March 17, 2009, in *Drug Safety & Health News*).

He always kind of reminded me of a cat, anyway.

But this just in, the always mischievous Senator Charles Grassley (kind of like out lolcats!) has written a letter to President Barack Obama that says:

> One thing I've asked every president since Ronald
> Reagan to do is to hold a Rose Garden ceremony
> honoring whistleblowers. No one has done so yet, but I
> hope that you will, based on your strong statements
> about accountability in government. I'm writing this
> letter to urge you to do so.

Can the Lolcats come? If so, we're in!

WE CUM TO ROZ GARDEN NAIM THE DAE!

It seems that pharma's friends within the FDA are not quite ready to jump into the rose garden celebration. A recent memo just went around reminding FDAers about "trade secrets", in other words not spilling the beans on pharma. I've heard that one before. It applies to pretty much everyone from wining and dining to gifting payoffs and other unlovlies. In fact, in spite of the much-vaunted laws requiring disclosure of payments to physicians in Vermont and a few other states, over half of the payments are not disclosed under the guise of "trade secret", but they are not required to provide any proof of that, in other words it is a bunch of bs.

Pills, Shills, and the Psychiatry Wars

Hat tip to Nancy Fruge.

Chapter 59: More Evidence That Clinical Practice Guidelines are Bullshit

(Originally posted March 17, 2009, in *Drug Safety & Health News*).

I've blogged previously about how clinical practice guidelines are bullshit and that about half of them are based on little or no evidence whatsoever. And now it is clear that most of the doctors who are writing these guidelines are on the payroll of the pharmaceutical industry. And that these guidelines are used for 'follow the guidelines or you aren't following the standard of care' kind of bs (see "How Much Ya Gonna Pay Me for Those Medical Guidelines").

Now we have more evidence that the guidelines really are just infomercials to promote utilization of prescription medications. An article in *JAMA* asserts that the entire process of the development of "expert guidelines" is problematic.[139] They go on to state that:

> *Guidelines often have become marketing tools for device and pharmaceutical manufacturers. While the ACC and AHA receive no industry funding for guideline development, they do receive industry support to disseminate guideline products such as pocket guides. Financial ties between guideline panel members and industry are common. "Experts" on guideline panels are more likely to receive industry funding for research, consulting fees, and speakers' honoraria.*

Other news in *JAMA* this week is that physicians should be taught to be more conservative in their drug prescribing behavior. Something we have always advocated here at the *Drug Safety & Health News*. Too often we whip out the prescription pad with the attitude that it "can't hurt." Well with 106,000 deaths each year related to prescription medications, I wouldn't agree that this is the case.

Remember this guy?

Deaths from prescription medications, most commonly pain killers and benzodiazepines and other sedatives, are on the rise, and now more commonly result in death than the abuse of non-prescription drugs, like heroin and cocaine.

Hat tip to CDC mole.

Chapter 60: Prostate Screening Found to be Useless

(Originally posted March 19, 2009, in *Drug Safety & Health News*).

This just in from *The New England Journal of Medicine*, two large studies adding further evidence that much of our medical screening and interventions are doing more harm than good, this time with the Prostate Specific Antigen (PSA) test, which is used to screen for prostate cancer in men. For the past twenty years, yearly PSA screening with rectal exam has been recommended, based, of course, on little or no evidence that it is useful, just the assumption that it "couldn't hurt" or "if I had a cancer, I'd want to get it out." So most American men get the tests. The Europeans do it much less commonly, as one of them pointed out "we think differently about these kinds of things than the Americans."

Oui, oui.

So, on to the studies. The first study from the Americans, the Prostate, Lung, Colon and Ovarian (PLCO) Cancer Screening Study, involved 76,693 men who were randomly assigned to receive PSA screening and rectal exam every year for six years or have usual care. Although more prostate cancer was diagnosed in the screened group, they didn't have more prostate cancer related deaths after seven years.[140]

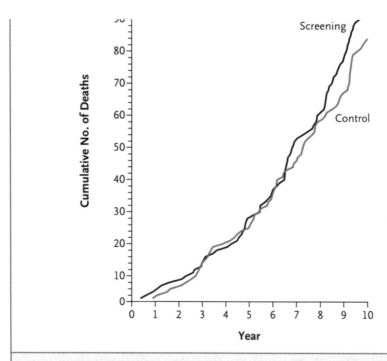

Figure 1. Number of Diagnoses of All Prostate Cancers (Panel A) and Number of Prostate-Cancer Deaths (Panel B).

More prostate cancer diagnosed, but no difference in prostate cancer death rates.

After ten years there were no differences in deaths between those who got screened (50) and those who did not (44), a 13% higher death rate in the screened group that wasn't statistically significant.

In the European Randomized Study of Screening for Prostate Cancer 182,000 men age 55-74 were randomly assigned to PSA screening every four years or not receive screening and followed for an average of nine years.[141] There were more prostate cancer diagnoses and 20% fewer prostate cancer deaths in the screened group, a difference that was statistically significant. The absolute difference was 0.71 per 1000 men meaning 1,410 men would need to be screened and 48 men treated to prevent one prostate cancer death. There was no difference in overall death rates.

Dr. B's comment: Not all cancers are created equal. Most men identified as having abnormal tests will probably never develop a prostate cancer that will kill them (a similar situation holds for mammography). Prostate cancer screening is resulting in men getting a lot of unnecessary treatments that can be associated with impotence and incontinence. The lack of difference in death rates probably means that for every man "saved" from prostate cancer there is one who has died from radiation treatments when their prostate cancer never would have killed him in the first place.

Now read online, "When Do I Need to Go to the Doctor For My Enlarged Prostate?"[142]

[Update: The most recent update from the European Randomized Study of Screening for Prostate Cancer showed a reduction of Prostate Cancer of 27% at 13 years compared to those not screened. Overall mortality still was unchanged, with a relative risk of 1, meaning no effect.[143] The authors estimated an overdiagnosis rate of about 30%, meaning that 30% of the screened individuals probably would have died without ever having symptoms or knowing they had prostate cancer. These patients typically end up getting treatment, with additional side effects related to medications, surgery, and radiation, which can include impotence and secondary cancer from radiation. These secondary effects in the over-diagnosed patients represent one possible explanation for the lack of a difference in overall mortality between those who are screened and not screened.]

[Update 2: This original post kicked up a hornet's nest with a doctor blogger named David Gorski, M.D. He and a guy named Peter Lipson, M.D., had a thing going with what they called Science Based Bloggers where they made a cottage industry out of insulting average people who were anti-vaccine or pro-alternative medicine, what they called 'woo.' What really hit Gorski below the belt was that prostate screening and surgery was his daily bread and butter. After attacking me on this post him and Lipson went on to try and paint me as part of the 'anti-vaccine crowd' (I have since written about my support for COVID vaccines and vaccines in childhood, but continue to voice skepticism based on the evidence on vaccines for the flu (even though my employer, Emory University, requires me to get one) and HPV.]

Chapter 61: Update from Mrs. Bremner from the American Heart Association Meeting on Salt and Hypertension

(Originally posted March 20, 2009, in *Drug Safety & Health News*).

Mrs. Bremner is in Tampa FL this week attending the American Heart Association (AHA) Epidemiology meeting. And having a good time too as she has texted me (don't have TOO good a time, Mrs. Bremner!). The most inspiring talk she has seen is about salt and health,[144] delivered by Dr. G. A. MacGregor from the University of London, someone she described as a VERY inspirational speaker (hopefully not TOO inspiring, Mrs. Bremner!).

Our daughter told me that she doesn't like it when I call her mother Mrs. Bremner. She thinks it is demeaning. And sounds bad. For those readers who haven't caught on (Duh!), my wife kept her own name when we married (she's not REALLY Mrs. Bremner, SORRY!), which is entirely reasonable since we are academics, and she already had a string of papers under her belt when we married that she would lose 'credit' for if she changed her name.

That is fine and good, but I wasn't prepared for the fact that she would give our first born the name 'Vaccarino Bremner' as a last name. I wasn't around when they gave her the form to fill out the application for the birth certificate. I guess it serves us guys right for not being *around*. It was a little awkward though when we went to Mexico and had a hard time getting into the country cuz her passport didn't match her plane ticket. That is when we had to break the news to our little cherubin that she wasn't REALLY a Bremner!

Sob!

I named my son James Douglas Bremner III but when he actually popped out of Mrs Bremner's (sic) belly he looked more Mexican than Scottish, so I had to acknowledge that the Sicilian genes had wiped out the last trace of the brave Scottish freedom fighter from the family line. As do I. Mrs. Bremner suggested that we should ALL change our names to 'Vaccarino Bremner.'

Doy!

Anyway/hoo back to salt. Excessive salt intake in the diet is the leading cause for increases in high blood pressure (hypertension). And increases in untreated hypertension are a leading cause for heart and kidney disease. Salt was originally introduced into the diet in China 5,000 years ago as a way to preserve food during the winter. Unfortunately, we have a natural proclivity toward salt, and our current consumption of salt is 50 times what it was 10,000 years ago. Salt tends to result in a retention of water in the kidneys, which leads to high blood pressure. Countries who have taken a concerted effort to lower salt in the diet, like Japan and the United Kingdom, have seen a drop in hypertension and heart disease. Most salt in the US diet is from processed foods and from soft drinks. Salt improves the taste of tasteless food, prolongs the life of food, and retains the weight of processed foods, all of which are advantage to food companies, so they tend to put a lot of salt in food.

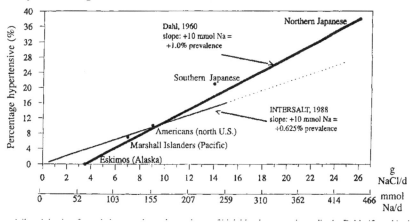

Correlation between salt consumption and high blood pressure.

Data above is from the INTERSALT trial. The data is conclusive that salt contributes to high blood pressure.

215

Several studies have shown that populations who migrate from countries where salt is not available to those where it is available have an increase in hypertension.

Stay away from processed foods, the "center of the grocery store", and remember that canned foods are high in sodium. Eating out at fast foods restaurants will get you a high sodium hit. Cook your own meals whenever possible.

Now read online, "Getting Blood Pressure Under Control Without Medications."[145]

Chapter 62: The Story of Modern Medicine, by Pharma Giles

(Originally posted March 21, 2009, in *Drug Safety & Health News*).

Series 606B

Here is a carefully planned reference book which will help to answer the many questions that lively children ask.

Interesting and accurate information about the modern pharmaceutical industry is given within the limits of a relatively simple vocabulary. Even children whose reading experience is limited will be encouraged by the carefully prepared text and magnificent illustrations to find out for themselves, and at the same time gain extra reading practice.

A LADYBIRD
"ACHIEVEMENTS"
BOOK

75p
NET

A LADYBIRD "ACHIEVEMENTS" BOOK

THE STORY OF MODERN MEDICINE

By
HENRY McKINNELL, MBA.
With illustrations by
PHARMA GILES

Published by Sue, Grabbit & Runne, Nether Wallop
First published in 1994   ©   Printed in England

Have you ever been ill and had to go to the doctor? If you have, you doctor will probably have given you a medicine to help you get better.

People don't have to be ill to be given medicines. They can also take medicines to stop being unhappy, to give up smoking, or (if they are old men) to keep their much younger girlfriends happy.

People of all ages take medicines. The picture shows Dick and Jane going to the Chemist with their Mummy. Their teacher at school has said that Dick and Jane are sometimes naughty.

The teacher told Dick and Jane's Mummy to see their Doctor. The Doctor gets paid lots of money by a pharmaceutical company to say nice things about a certain type of medicine that makes children quiet.

He has told Dick and Jane's Mummy to go to the Chemists to get them some.

218

Medicines are special chemicals that can help sick people to get better.

Most medicines are made by pharmaceutical companies.

Because sick people want to get better, new medicines are very expensive. This means that pharmaceutical companies make lots of money.

Sometimes, medicines are so expensive that poor people cannot afford them, and have to carry on being sick.

This is called "supply side economics", and makes sure that the very rich people who are in charge of pharmaceutical companies can carry on being very rich.

Unlike poor people.

But poor people are not important, because they don't have any money.

Medicines are invented by clever people called scientists.

They work in very nice buildings called laboratories. These laboratories cost lots of money, which is why new medicines are so expensive.

The scientists sit around all day, drinking coffee and talking, until one of them has an idea for a brand new medicine.

The scientists then go and tell their manager about their new idea, and ask for some money to pay for making some of the new medicine to test.

The scientist's manager is an even cleverer person called a "Master of Business Administration", or "MBA" for short.

The MBA's job is to say that the scientist's new medicine is an unacceptable Business Risk, and that instead, the scientists should make medicines just like the ones that all of the other pharmaceutical companies are making.

This is called "innovation".

New medicines have to be tested to make sure that they can make sick people better. First of all, they are tested on animals.

If animals don't die when they are given the new medicine, it can be tested on sick people. This is called a "clinical trial".

Sometimes, the sick people in clinical trials become even sicker when they are given the new medicine.

If this happens, the new medicine is said to have "side effects".

If a new medicine has side effects, the rich people who run pharmaceutical companies sometimes get very upset.

They will tell the people who run clinical trials not to tell anyone about the side-effects.

This makes everyone happy again and lets the rich people get richer by letting them sell their new medicines without any silly rules about safety getting in the way.

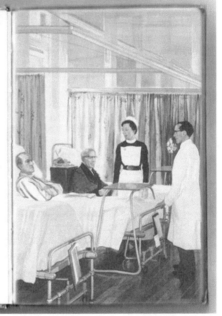

Sometimes, new medicines give sick people such bad side effects that they become very ill indeed. The families of the sick people then often get very upset, and go to see some clever people who are cleverer than scientists, and even cleverer than MBAs.

These people are called lawyers. Lawyers try to make the pharmaceutical companies give some money to the sick people who have been made ill by the new medicine.

This is called "compensation". The rich people who run pharmaceutical companies do not like paying compensation, because this means that there is less money for them to have.

Pharmaceutical companies have their own lawyers, who are cleverer than anyone else's lawyers.

They argue with the sick people's lawyers. Sometimes, they argue for so long that the sick people give up or die.

This saves the pharmaceutical companies paying lots of compensation for making people ill.

The rich people who run pharmaceutical companies are called Executives. They are all MBAs and are often lawyers as well. Their job is to pretend that their new medicines don't make lots of people sick, even when they do.

Sometimes though, so many people get ill because of a new medicine that the Government eventually tells the pharmaceutical company to stop selling it, and makes the company pay lots of compensation instead.

The Executives never have to pay compensation themselves however, because they are very rich and clever and also have lots of friends in the Government.

Sometimes, people who work for pharmaceutical companies go and tell the Executives that making people ill just to make money isn't very nice, and that they will tell the Government about it all.

These people are called "Whistleblowers". Executives do not like whistleblowers, but then no-one likes tell-tales, do they? That is why Whistleblowers don't have any friends.

Some new medicines make people sick in a way that doctors do not always see. Look at the man on the ledge of the building in the picture. He has been taking a new medicine to help him give up smoking, but it is has made him very unhappy and upset.

The man talking to him is a pharmaceutical public relations consultant.

He is trying to stop the man taking the final step that will make sure that he never smokes again, even though that is what the new medicine is supposed to do.

Such a thing is called "bad publicity", and the consultant does not want that to happen. It is often a side-effect of new medicines that lots of doctors and pharmaceutical companies also don't like to talk about.

If a new medicine gets bad publicity, the Executives will put lots of advertisements on television to tell everybody that the new medicine is fine but that it might make some people ill.

This makes everything OK.

This pretty lady is a pharmaceutical sales representative. Her clothes are quite small because most doctors are men and most men like to see pretty ladies in small clothes.

The sales lady's job is to persuade the doctor to buy new medicines from her company to give to the sick people who come to see him, despite any "side effects" the medicine may have.

Sometimes she gives the doctor nice presents or money to help him decide to buy the new medicine. Or perhaps she will pay for him to go on a nice holiday, where he can tell other doctors about how good the new medicine is.

This is called "marketing" and helps doctors, the pharmaceutical companies and their executives get even richer.

There are lots of pharmaceutical sales representatives. Sometimes, they form a queue in the Doctor's office. This helps to cut down the number of sick people that the doctor has to see.

223

New medicines are made in big factories like this one.

Scientists take lots of poisonous chemicals, and mix them up in big tanks. You can see the big tanker delivering poisonous chemicals to the factory in this picture.

When all of the poisonous chemicals are properly mixed, they are turned into medicines.

The medicine is then mixed with sugar to make pills.

Scientists test the pills to make sure that they have been made properly before they are sent to doctors. If the tests find something wrong, then the pills have to be destroyed.

If the pills are very valuable though, bad results are sometimes changed to make the pills seem OK.

This is called "Risk-Based Quality Assurance" and helps the pharmaceutical companies make even more money.

When a pharmaceutical company makes a new medicine, its lawyers make sure that no-one else can make the same medicine. This is called "patent protection".

Patent protection means that pharmaceutical companies can make lots of money by charging sick people as much as they like for a new medicine, without anyone being allowed to make the medicine more cheaply.

Patent protection does not last forever though. When a new medicine isn't new any more, companies called "generics" are also allowed to make the medicine. They can often sell it to sick people for much less money.

Look how hard the patent lawyers are working. They don't want the generic companies to sell cheaper medicines. That would mean there would be less money for the big pharmaceutical company Executives.

When Executives feel that they might not have as much money for themselves, they get very upset. They try to find ways of making sure that they can still stay rich and important.

Because making medicines is quite expensive, Executives often close the medicine factories and fire all of the workers to cut costs, just to make sure that there is still plenty of money left for them.

They also close the laboratories where all of the scientists drink coffee and invent new medicines, and fire all of the scientists as well.

This "cost cutting" means that new medicines can't be invented or made, and that sick people won't have better medicines in the future.

But at least the Executives of the pharmaceutical companies get to stay very rich and live happily ever after.

Isn't the pharmaceutical industry wonderful?

[Update: Pharma Giles was one of many anonymous posters who, like ClinPsych, the MacGuffin, and PharmaGossip, came and went during the heady times of the *Drug Safety and Health News* blog. Destination, unknown.]

Chapter 63: DSM-5 Shadow Team Strikes Back at Psychiatric Establishment on PTSD

(Originally posted March 24, 2009, in *Drug Safety & Health News*).

Since the establishment of the DSM-5 Shadow Team to track the proceedings of the DSM committee in response to their paranoid decision to keep all of their meetings a secret and not allow anyone to keep notes or talk to the press, we have been quietly reviewing psychiatric nosology and contemplating the architecture of psychiatry. The ongoings of the "mainstream" DSM committee were chronicled in an article in this months' *Time* magazine (remember when you used to read that? So, do I) called "Redefining Crazy: Researchers Revise the DSM-V" where it made the point that psychiatrists were spending more time arguing than coming to consensus (Hey Dr Hyman, I thought you weren't supposed to talk to the press? I am gonna have to tattle on you to David).

However, several recent articles by journalists who seem to have granted themselves honorary degrees in psychiatry and who quote whatever ridiculous opinion from psychiatrists that happens to cross their desk as if it is, well, worth quoting, have prompted us to speak out.

First off, *The New York Times* wrote an exceedingly lame editorial[146] regarding the decision of the Department of Defense to not award the Purple Heart (the medal received by soldiers who are wounded in combat) for combat-related posttraumatic stress disorder (PTSD).[147] Here is their lame comment:

> *PTSD can be difficult to diagnose, with symptoms that can arise later in life, far from the battlefield and are not necessarily linked to any specific actions of an enemy. So, the Pentagon contends that it has no choice but to exclude its sufferers from the Purple Heart, given to those whose injuries result from direct and intentional action by the enemy...*

> *The military is, in fact, moving forward merely by mentioning PTSD and the Purple Heart in the same breath. Imagine Gen. George Patton, who so notoriously slapped a quivering enlisted man, learning that his beloved Army was even considering giving medals to those whose combat tours left them mentally shattered.*

Frankly I found this letter to be patently offensive, ill informed, and incorrect. First off, General Patton was an idiot, and should not be celebrated for physically abusing soldiers. Secondly, PTSD is very much related to combat exposure, is not difficult to diagnose, and is not delayed in onset. The *NYT* morons go on to opine that "Purple Heart may not be the answer — not until, perhaps, advances in brain science bring full objectivity to the diagnosis of mental injury." And exactly what "brain science" is that? The same morons who publicized dubious science such as the search for the neural correlates of morality or trumpeted a drug that would preserve marital fidelity are now turning those brain scanners against the recognition that war is hell and can be associated with life-long mental wounds?

Next on the journalist role call is an article in *Scientific American* called, Soldier's Stress: What Doctors Get Wrong About PTSD, by David Dobbs.[148] An example of one of his (highlighted) retarded statements is "misdiagnosed soldiers receive the wrong treatments and risk becoming mired in a Veterans Administration system that encourages chronic disability." Since when does the VA want chronic disability? If anything, they are invested in reducing their costs. And who is he to say who is "misdiagnosed"? Not everyone develops PTSD, but for those who do, it is real, believe me, and it doesn't matter what some pointy headed professors (or journalists) who are seeking attention with provocative statements say.

Dobbs taps into an underbelly of academic psychiatry that looks for approval from others by trying to look like they buck the trend about trauma and PTSD, with the basic message that PTSD is an overblown diagnosis created by a bunch of cry-babies. Most of these "detractors" he quotes were authors of articles in a moronic special issue of the *Journal of Anxiety Disorders* in 2007 on PTSD. These authors purport to be offering important and controversial papers that will undermine the diagnosis of PTSD but instead they just send up a bunch of hot air balloons. Simon Wessely, a psychiatrist from the Institute of Psychiatry in London, writes a convoluted "historical" piece that seems to imply that we should pay attention to the role of secondary gain (e.g., getting disability benefits) in the development of PTSD. Big deal, some people want disability payments, does that mean PTSD is a bullshit diagnosis? I don't think so. It would have been more interesting if Simon had written a piece telling us about who was the mystery woman at his institute involved in the Sex and Seroquel scandal who said that she needed to be punished by the head of the Seroquel Study Team for reading a paper about Risperdal.

Next in the *Journal* we have Richard McNally, who gets a lot of mileage out of pointing to his study showing that people who think they were abducted by aliens have psychophysiological responses that look like PTSD as evidence that PTSD is a bs diagnosis (if those aliens did that to my rectum, I think I would have PTSD too, wouldn't you)? He makes the point that if you tightened the criteria for PTSD that there would be fewer veterans classified as having PTSD (based on an article that revised the estimate downward from 14% to 9%). So what? As we pointed out in a letter to *Science* in 2007 that still would mean 236,000 Vietnam veterans with PTSD 30 years later.

Richard J. McNally, Ph.D.

Last time I saw Richard he broke his glasses down the middle during a lecture he was giving and had to hold up one half to read his slides, which he called his "monocle", which together with his spirited presentation made him look like a mad professor, indeed.

Next, we have Paul McHugh, M.D., the evil troll who used to second as chairman of psychiatry at Johns Hopkins School of Medicine in Baltimore. Last time I saw him lecture he was whining about one of his "case reports" of a woman claiming childhood sexual abuse "how could that woman have been sexually abused by her father? That family was one of the most prominent families in Baltimore!" as if that made any frigging difference. They write:

> PTSD, as presently diagnosed, described, and treated,
> has failed to improve on what had been standard
> teaching. It has redefined and overextended the reach of
> a long-recognized natural human reaction of fear,
> anxiety, and conditioned emotional reactions to shocks
> and traumas.

In other words, nothing like the old days, when guys killed Japs and enjoyed it, and gals got raped and if they didn't stop sniveling you could just give them a good wack to help them get over it.

PTSD doesn't exist cuz I said so. So shut up and sit down.

Robert Spitzer wrote an editorial in this special issue which promised a radical revision, but instead merely recommended requiring that the person be personally exposed to the traumatic event, and dropped a few of the symptom criteria like irritability that were not

229

specific to PTSD.[149] Another editorial was written by the sociologist Allan Young and the epidemiologist Naomi Breslau. Last time I saw Allan he was reading a paper about the Yale Neurosciences PTSD program as an object for study by sociologists with the basic thesis that PTSD is a "social construct." Frankly when I see a sociologist who studies mental health my instinct is to run in the opposite direction as quickly as I can. For what it's worth here is the abstract of their paper. Let me know if you can understand it. I sure as hell couldn't:

> *As represented in the DSMs, the PTSD syndrome coheres through cause-and-effect relations among diagnostic features. Research practices routinely ignore this essential characteristic, by atomizing the diagnostic features, especially the role of memory. The failure to confront this contradiction explains the failure of research to fully engage the pathological process that justifies the PTSD diagnostic classification. Several papers in this collection direct readers' attention to this fundamental problem. We are pessimistic that their insight will lead to positive results.*

They don't sound very optimistic. Does that mean they are not resilient and are vulnerable to PTSD? Don't worry guys if you get sick, I'll make sure that you do not go on disability and become chronic charges of the government.

What these guys are saying is that PTSD is "not reliable, not accepted" often made up to get victims' compensation and compare that to "accepted" diagnoses like major depression and bipolar. What's more their cronies on the mainstream DSM want to drop Dissociative Disorders as diagnoses all together, for no better reason than because they, well, want to. Well, I've got news for you guys just because drug companies made billions off of the pedaling of depression (and not PTSD) doesn't make that disorder somehow more "real." And the suffering of patients with PTSD and

Dissociative Disorders for that matter is very real, thank you very much.

Bye now.

[Update] David Dobbs had a cow after I wrote this post and wrote a very angry response that showed up high on google searches about me for the next several years. Looking back on it makes me reflect that I am glad I didn't decide to go to journalism school after all.

Chapter 64: Obama Healthcare Plans Unlikely to Get Much Traction

(Originally posted March 25, 2009, in *Drug Safety & Health News*).

This President Barack Obama's administration is <u>rolling back into universal healthcare land</u> just like Hillary Clinton tried to way back when.[150] We'll see if he can survive the shark infested waters any better than she did.

Come on in, the water's fine.

In case you are Rip van Winkle, or someone dropped you on your head, so you don't remember, back in 1993 Hillary Clinton got torn to shreds by insurance lobbyists and other special interest groups. Remember the Harry and Louise ads funded by the Health Insurance Association of American (HIAA), where they sit around fretting about how to pay for their mandatory healthcare insurance?

Harry and Louise worrying over their medical bills.

Now the health insurance guys are whining again. They say they don't want a "Medicare for all" plan cuz it will drive them all out of business. Or if there is an expanded healthcare, they don't want the government to have the chance to negotiate contracts with doctors and hospitals (unlike them). Oh, and if the government can negotiate with doctors and hospitals, they will go out of business too. But isn't that anti-capitalist to be against negotiating prices? What they might as well say is that they are bloated and inefficient and couldn't compete with any alternative system. I call the organizations that represent hospitals, insurance, doctors and drug companies the evil Gang of Four.

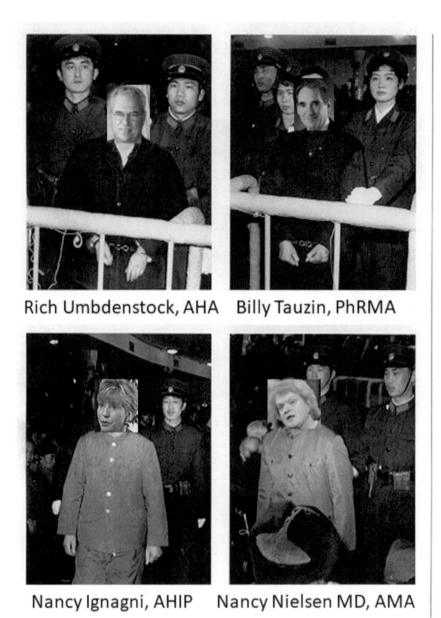

Rich Umbdenstock, AHA   Billy Tauzin, PhRMA

Nancy Ignagni, AHIP   Nancy Nielsen MD, AMA

Clockwise from upper left, AMA, HIAA, PhRMA, AHA

Did you know that Ronald Reagan made promotional videos for the American Medical Association (AMA) that they showed to their members way back in the day, about how they should fight against Medicare, because it was socialized medicine? The AMA really has a disgraceful history, and I am glad that their flagship journal, JAMA, is running into rocky shores. The insurance guys and their pals the hospital lobby (American Hospital Association, AHA), the AMA, and pharma (Pharmaceutical Research and Manufacturer's Association (PhRMA) are gonna do what they can to confuse and confound. But in the meantime, they have offered to not charge people more for insurance who have pre-existing medical conditions, if everyone is required to buy insurance.[151] This looks like a crumb they are throwing out to try and avoid any new government insurance program or expansion of Medicare.

Hmmm, do we want more government control, or less of it? More government control, or less? Hmmm.

Maybe we should set up an office pool to see how long "healthcare reform" lasts this time around.

Chapter 65: Gimme That Old Time Religion: It's Called Morality

(Originally posted March 25, 2009, in *Drug Safety and Health News*).

In this recent piece from Howard Brody, M.D., of the blog, *Hooked: Ethics, Medicine, and Pharma*, about how the American Psychiatric Association (APA) recently voted to eliminate pharmaceutical industry funding of educational symposia as well as free meals etc. from their annual meeting, he asks what they will do to pay for their education.[152] I am not involved in the politics of the APA (or any other organization, for that matter).

The last time I went to an APA meeting it was in New York several years ago and I took my daughter so we could have a bonding experience and see the sights. I typically have gone to the American College of Neuropsychopharmacology (ACNP), which doesn't have overt drug sales displays, so I am going to have to look into doing something at APA given these new rules. And hat tip to Danny Carlat who has gotten involved in the internal politics of education within the APA and surely must have played a role in this decision.

The fact is that the APA is the first medical organization to make such a move and hats off to them. Let's celebrate.

Howard quoted someone from the APA saying that without drug companies they would have to hold their lectures at the YMCA. Well, I think I have a pretty good analogy for you. For one of our NIH funded grants, we added as a consultant Lori Davis, M.D., of the Tuscaloosa VA and the University of Alabama Birmingham Department of Psychiatry. Lori came over to Atlanta and gave a lecture on "Diagnosis and Treatment of PTSD" and then met with our staff and fellows to review diagnostic assessments of PTSD. She will return in May. The lecture was delivered in the auditorium of the old Georgia Mental Hospital which is now owned by Emory and called Emory Briarcliff. Not the Ritz, but no overhead, free, easy, and free of commercial influence. Isn't that the way it should be?

No, this is not a Stalinist era building in East Berlin. This is where Dr. Davis gave her pharma-free lecture on PTSD, and the home of corporate headquarters for the *Drug Safety & Health News* Blog

We'd be happy to have some more pharma free CME if you don't mind our humble quarters. We could get our pals within driving distance to come over and give a lecture. Hell, I'd be glad to give a lecture where someone doesn't tell me 'Go out and sell some Paxil Doug!' Ya'll come over and let's have us a pig pickin'!

[Update] The Emory Briarcliff campus is where the television series *Stranger Things* was filmed. Millie Bob Brown is allegedly a major fan of the *Drug Safety & Health News* blog, which may be why the star of the series was attracted to the idea of filming where the corporate headquarters were previously located.

Chapter 66: Doctors from Different Disciplines Examine an Interesting Case

(Originally posted March 25, 2009, in *Drug Safety & Health News*).

Readers of the *Drug Safety & Health News* know that they can always count on interesting detours from the usual boring news on drug safety and health on this blog, although the former topics are always served up with gusto and enthusiasm. Today we have an interesting Alt CME (Alternative Continuing Medication Education, always free of interference from drug companies) case that was approached by doctors of different disciplines.

A 33-year-old white female developed the sudden onset of nausea, vomiting, and changes in mental status. She had signs of a cold for the past several days but had attended a concert by the jazz signer Pearl Bailey on a Thursday and a fund-raising dinner for the State of Washington art museum on Friday. On February 12, 1966, a Saturday morning she awoke with headache, vomiting, and change in consciousness. She was driven to the Olympia (Washington) Hospital where she was treated with the antibiotic tetracycline intravenously and underwent lumbar puncture. She was transferred to University Hospital in Seattle but died en route.

Laurnell Bremner, the year before she died.

So here come the other doctors. Some friends of hers who had been meeting weekly with a psychic named Dr. Ralph Duby asked him what he thought about the sudden death of their friend. He asked what medications she had received and when them told him, he put his finger to the side of his nose and said "shhhhhhhh!" and that that drug could cause meningitis. To complete my medical education I was sent a book called *There is a River*,[153] about the life of Edgar Cayce, an uneducated man who would go into trances and "diagnose" people with a range of medical conditions.

Edgar Cayce

There is a river, and all streams flow into it.

When I heard this news I looked in the literature and found out about a syndrome called <u>Drug Induced Aseptic Meningitis (DIAM)</u>,[154] which results from exposure to antibiotics or anti-inflammatory drugs, and which is often seen in people with <u>uveitis</u> (an autoimmune inflammation of the eye, seen in several of her children, which is associated with a genetic variant called HLA B27, which is also associated with spondyloarthropathy, which she suffered from).

In the course of doing some research on the house we lived in at Fish Trap, a rural area on Puget Sound outside of Olympia, WA, I called <u>Ward Miles M.D.</u>,[155] a local physician who started Group Health in Olympia and who lived in my childhood home for many years after we left. Miles bought the property and built a lovely farm in the back yard with sheep, whose wool is currently being converted into a scarf by Mrs. Bremner (keep up the good work, Penelope!). When I told Miles about the medical history, he was confused about it and said it

didn't make sense.

Sheep at the Fish Trap house.

My son's pediatrician said that if she got antibiotics before they drew the cultures, which could account for why they didn't have a definitive diagnosis on the coroner's report.

My uncle, <u>William Bremner, M.D., Ph.D.</u>, who is Chairman of Medicine at the University of Washington in Seattle[156] and who was intimately involved in these events, says that as a first-year medical student at the U. of Washington at the time that he thought it strange that an adult would be infected with Haemophilus influenzae bacterial meningitis, since that is typically only seen in children.

William Bremner, M.D., Ph.D.

However, when I called my father about it, he told me that the cerebrospinal fluid from the lumbar puncture of my mother's lumbar puncture (he was a medical doctor present at the procedure) was "full of puss", consistent with a bacterial infection (i.e., not drug induced aseptic meningitis).

As Edgar Cayce would attest to, life is full of mysteries, sometimes things don't make sense, and sometimes we don't get a definitive diagnosis.

But since this CME is not funded by the pharmaceutical industry, we don't have to come to a definitive conclusion, like take this drug for that condition.

Another advantage of Alt CME.

Chapter 67: America's Doctor Outed as Drug Pimp

(Originally posted March 26, 2009, in *Drug Safety & Health News*).

People have told me that I should go on Oprah because of my book about medications.[157] But I am glad I never did (not that I got the offer anyway) after learning about how Dr. Mehmet Oz, described as America's Doctor, who makes frequent appearances on the Oprah Show and who authored several books in the popular series of You: The Owner's Manual which he co-authors with Michael Roizen, M.D.,[158] is a paid consultant for a website called RealAge[159] that asks you a series of questions to find out your biological or "real" age. The web site has registered 27 million people.

Turns out this web site collects demographic information and sells its services to drug companies, who then use it to target specific groups to sell prescription medications to. For instance, if it turned out that you were at risk for pre-hypertension, they would send you emails with "information", and then when you were "softened up" hit you up with a pitch about how you should take a medication for hypertension. Which all means, of course, that Dr. Oz gets automatic admission to the *Drug Safety & Health News* blog team of M.D. Cheerleaders for Pharma!

I was actually on their radio show right after my book came out, interviewed by Dr. Michael Roizen, but that is as close as I ever got to the bright lights. It is actually kind of weird how much the media shies away from the issue of prescription medication safety, unless they have the feeling that "everyone else is going after the story."

The newspaper article on the topic quoted a woman who appropriately stated that she didn't appreciate having her personal information used for drug marketing. But then the article (I guess to have "balance"?) bizarrely quoted a former pharmaceutical saleswoman who stated that it is important to have all the information you can get so you can make informed decisions for yourself.

"Information"? Give me a break. And my comment on Dr. Oz's behavior is go back and read your Hippocratic Oath, which sez above all do no harm. And sending blanket emails with scary messages to induce people to take prescription medications which could hurt them and that they may not need is a violation of that oath.

Hat tip to therapy patient.

Now read online, "What Causes High Blood Pressure?"[160]

Chapter 68: Salt and Hypertension: Mrs. Bremner Strikes Back

(Originally posted March 27, 2009, in *Drug Safety & Health News*).

Last week Mrs. Bremner was communicating to us from the American Heart Association Meeting about the importance of salt on blood pressure and health which led to a post about the topic which led to a lively discussion. David Colquhoun started out by pointing out that the graph showing a correlation between salt load and hypertension from the paper by Professor MacGregor could be accounted for by four data points. Mrs. Bremner countered by pointing out that they had re-analyzed the results without the four lowest data points and it was still significant. She subsequently pointed to another paper which summarizes clinical trials on the effects of salt reduction in the diet on health.[161]

In this paper the authors point out that many studies that are used to argue that salt reduction has no effect on hypertension or health are studies in which the salt reduction only occurred over the course of one week or involved acute salt depletion. The authors point out that one week is not long enough to evaluate the effects of salt reduction, and that acute salt reduction leads to an activation of the sympathetic nervous system, which leads to an artificial increase in blood pressure. Sounds good to me so far, guys.

They listed 17 trials of people with hypertension and 11 trials of people with normal blood pressure that were conducted for four weeks or more and had adequate salt reduction (4.6 g per day) as measured by excretion in the urine. People with hypertension had a 5 mm Hg point drop in systolic and 3-point drop in diastolic. People with normal blood pressure also showed a drop to a lesser extent. The authors note that this amount of salt reduction would result in a 14% drop in strokes and a 9% drop in heart deaths.

Unfortunately, no one has done a randomized trial of low salt versus high salt diet, and it is unlikely to happen now due to ethical issues.

Mrs. Bremner points out that increases in salt in the diet lead to a craving for salty food that causes a vicious cycle, which is one way people may become addicted to salty junk foods and snack foods.

Dr B.'s comment: It looks like cutting down on salt does lower blood pressure although a 14% relative reduction in cardiac events may not be that big of a deal in terms of absolute reduction of risk for a single individual. Salt may be just part of the problem with junk food. There was a study showing that people who eat in fast food restaurants three times a week have a greater than 90% risk of getting diabetes or heart disease and I need to find that reference again.

Chapter 69: Captain Pill Takes a Shot Across the Bow over Validity of PTSD Diagnosis

(Originally posted March 28, 2009, in *Drug Safety & Health News Blog*).

Well, I thought my last post on PTSD (see "DSM V Team Strikes Back Against PTSD Establishment on PTSD") might at least flush out who the mystery woman psychiatrist is from the Sex and Seroquel scandal (it didn't) but it did provoke a reaction from David Dobbs, the author of the *Time* magazine article ("The PTSD Trap") that I took on as peddling pseudo-contrarian views. My beef was not with David, whose *Neuron Culture* blog makes for good reading, but with psychiatrists such as Paul McHugh, M.D., who give lectures saying that childhood abuse memories are implanted by therapists based on nothing more than his opinion, or by others making sweeping statements implying that PTSD is somehow problematic.

I guess David got upset that I called him retarded (actually I said his comment implying that the VA wanted to increase the ranks of the PTSD disabled was retarded, not him) and he took issue with my saying I am not part of the establishment (hey I am not on DSM committee and never get awards and stuff like that, unlike some of my more druggy friends). He and other bloggers on scienceblogs.com took issue with my picking on their friend, with *Neuroskeptic* blogger criticizing me for calling professors pointy headed (hey I have an old car and Rush Limbaugh is the only channel I get) and *Orac* from the blog *Respectful Insolence* (cool! I didn't know he read my blog!) said I was getting on his nerves, and he was going to pick a fight with me about cancer screening tests being more or less useless (see "Prostate Cancer Screening Found to be Useless") (Gasp! I slap you with my glove Sir!). Well since he is a cancer guy, I guess it is always hard to get a criticism of what is your bottom line.

LOLcat strikes back in defense of Dr. B.

But hey this is a blog for Christ's sake and that post set a new record for readers, so I guess people at least didn't think it was boring.

Now it looks like David is going to make me the subject of a journalism symposium (yeah! I love attention!) and with these successive volleys the Good Ship Pilleous is now sailing into battle in the PTSD Wars!

Tally ho and onward buckaroos!

Next read online, "Does Saw Palmetto Help Enlarged Prostate?"[162]

Chapter 70: Goodbye to You Too, Yaz

Yaz wasn't approved to treat PMDD and acne, and in any case, not all women have PMDD or untreated acne, even though the makers of Yaz probably wish that that was the case.

By <u>Doug Bremner, Contributor</u>

(Originally posted March 29, 2009, in <u>*The Huffington Post*</u>).

Bayer recently announced that it is going to spend $20 million for an advertising campaign to reverse the effects of its ad campaign promoting the oral birth control pill, Yaz, as effective for the ups and downs of daily life as well as zits and other skin blemishes and weight loss. This ad campaign was launched after Yaz was approved for birth control with added side benefits of helping premenstrual dysphoric disorder (PDD) and acne, however the ads showed women kicking around balloons that said stuff like "mood swings" and "fatigue" while they played the songs "Goodbye to You" or "We're Not Going to Take It."

Goodbye to you too, Yaz.

Following this they got admonished by the FDA which led to the unusual settlement of being forced to run an ad campaign to undo the effects of false advertising. You see, Yaz wasn't approved to treat PMDD and acne, and in any case not all women have PMDD or untreated acne, even though the makers of Yaz certainly wish that that was the case. It was also promoted as helping with weight loss, although the weight you lose is just water, and it does that promoting retention of potassium, which can cause heart problems.

In other words, they were promoting it as a lifestyle drug, like look good, get laid, and feel good about yourself. What more could women want? Anyhoo, in the new ads an actress looks into the camera and says:

> *You may have seen some Yaz commercials recently that were not clear. The F.D.A. wants us to correct a few points in those ads.*

Indeed. Well first of all, I really hate it when they take a perfectly good song and associate with some cheesy product. They should make musicians sign a contract that they will never sell out their tunes which run around in our heads.

Second, that $20 million is "chump change" as one commenter pointed out, after they have already made their billions promoting a product for something that it wasn't approved for, something that can be thought of as the cost of doing business, kind of like the billion that Eli Lilly paying as punishment for off label promotion of Zyprexa (olanzapine) not being a big deal when they made 20 billion out of the deal. Finally, no one pointed out the fact that Yaz (and her sister pill Yasmin) (as I have written about before in "Is Your Birth Control Pill Driving You Bananas?") is the most posted about medication on medications.com, with most of the women complaining about how it makes them more depressed and anxious.

How can it be that your birth control pill makes you depressed?

Birth control pills (or oral contraceptive pills, or OCPs) contain sex hormones related to estrogen and progesterone. Normally these sex hormones cycle throughout the month. In addition to controlling reproduction, they also have effects on the brain, which is why they can cause anxiety and depression.

Taking the pill effectively blunts the normal variation in hormones; it also eliminates ovulation, which also affects sexuality. In fact, one study showed that strippers who were ovulating made $15 more per hour than strippers who were not ovulating, and that strippers on the pill made significantly less than other strippers.[163]

You can read more about the relative risks of heart disease and cancer in women of different ages and smoking status in my prior post on this topic or my book. However, I recommend using an IUD as the safest form of birth control, condoms or a diaphragm.

Now read online, "Are Birth Control Pills Safe?"[164]

Chapter 71: Somewhat Lame Editorial on Conflicts of Interest from the American Journal of Psychiatry

(Originally posted March 29, 2009, in *Drug Safety & Health News*).

This month's *The American Journal of Psychiatry* has a somewhat lame article on conflicts of interest regarding the pharmaceutical industry and psychiatry.[165] Before I delve into this piece I must provide some background information, however. Psychiatry is divided into two sections, maybe three. The first section is the Key Opinion Leaders (KOL) group, the guys at the head of our field, a term made up by the drug company guys, not me. We also used to call them "Shining Lights." These guys rake in hundreds of thousands of dollars per year doing consulting, industry supported talks, and other gigs. This has been going on for thirty years or so, although it was always glossed over with the rationale that it was good for academe and industry to put heads together, and that we were educating the common psychiatrist on updates on drugs. Forget about the slightly slimy feeling it gave you, the fact that the Shining Lights were smart guys was hard to dispute. And who really cared, anyway?

Chemical imbalance? No more!

But to be a Shining Light it is not enough to be just brilliant; you have to grease the wheels a little bit with pharma.

The second group (don't they have a word for this in France?) are the practicing psychiatrist clinicians, who don't make mega bucks from speaking and consulting gigs with pharma, but who get free pens and dinners, and free parties at the annual meetings, and don't have to pay for their CME, cuz Pharma Big Brother pays for it for them. And they get their info from the Shining Lights, who say everything is A-OK. The third group I think are the junior academics who aspire to be Shining Lights. They are willing to labor and toil, making their Shining Light mentors look good with their productivity, hoping someday to be "in the lights"!

Fast forward to the present. The public is starting to get fed up with business as usual. And they are seeing that this enormous payoff to leaders in academic psychiatry has tainted them to push prescription medications in cases where they should have known better, to the detriment of treatments like psychotherapy and meditation, which could have helped some patients more.

In other words, evidence of harm.

Which gets me to the editorial, which I will analyze bit by bit.

> To many psychiatrists' dismay, unresolved conflicts of
> interest between parts of our profession and the
> pharmaceutical industry continue to be a focus of
> concern.

Dismay? You mean the guys who are raking in half a mil per year and don't want the party to stop? And what does unresolved mean? Do they need a COI psychotherapist? Why don't they just call a spade a spade? Pharma was paying KOLs with the express purpose of influencing them to be favorable to their drugs.

> The impact of investigations of conflicts of interest
> extends beyond their targets and potentially affects the
> credibility of all psychiatrists.

Yeah, like what I said, Senator Grassley, why don't you go investigate the cardiologists. Not only are they corrupt, but they are also jerks. Unlike us, corrupt but loveable neurotics.

> *Psychiatry is reexamining its standards and ethical
> boundaries for interactions with the pharmaceutical
> industry.*

Translation: The KOLs who brought to you this morality play today (who are pretty much all, incidentally, consulting and speaking for pharma) are considering whether to run for cover or keep on playing the same old tunes. I mean, psychiatrist on the street is not reexamining her standards, noo?

> *Our standards should address not only the conduct of
> high-profile opinion leaders, but also our responsibility
> as individual physicians to deliver to our patients the
> highest-quality evidence-based medicine.*

Translation: We're thinking about you little guys! Here's a crumb!

I guess that's the way the cookie crumbles, as they say. (Source: Wikipedia: By Jonathunder - Own work, GFDL 1.2)

They go on:

> *There is no clearer example of conflict of interest than
> the participation of prominent psychiatrists in*

*pharmaceutical company speakers' bureaus, which
supply academic opinion leaders to deliver company-
approved presentations that market their drugs to their
clinical colleagues in the guise of medical education.*

Does that mean no more fees for lectures? Sound like a good idea to
me. How about medical ground rounds? Those are typically paid for
by pharma. I gave Grand Rounds last year at a university where the
pharma sponsors wouldn't pay for me, so my hosts had to scramble
to find funds to cover my trip. They go on:

*Conflicts arise when interests that once seemed
congruent begin to diverge. For the pioneers of
psychopharmacology, the pharmaceutical companies
were invaluable allies.*

Yeah, the good ole days of early psychopharmacology at early
meetings of the neuropsychopharmacologists (see "A Dissenting
View from the ACNP on Antidepressants"). They continue:

*As psychopharmacology has matured, education about
biological treatment has often narrowed to carefully
orchestrated marketing of specific drugs that may have
only marginal advantages over other drugs in the same
class. As the differences have become smaller, the
amount of money involved in marketing has become
greater.*

Hmmm. No comment. I'll have to meditate on that one. Like a Koan.

*Most of us may never receive a check from a
pharmaceutical company.*

That means you, little guy clinicians! Kiss kiss!

*The subsidy that each of us has been receiving is part of
what has fueled the excesses that are currently under
investigation.*

So, does that mean the party is over guys? I don't know about you,
but my attention span has been exceeded. In the future I will post
about Dr B.'s perfect Department of Psychiatry.

Cheers for Now.

Kiss kiss!

More reactions to the editorial here[166] and here.[167]

[Update: The Editor-in-Chief of *The American Journal of Psychiatry* at the time of this post, Robert Freedman, M.D., was also the editor who published our paper "Effects of isotretinoin on brain function,"[168] in the same journal, and caved to the drug company, Roche, when threatened with legal action as they tried to get our paper retracted (which was a threat to their billion dollar a year acne medication) by asking my university to do an inquiry. I always thought that was extremely cowardly of him. I mean, any time a drug company doesn't like a result that hurts their profits (even if it means potentially saves lives) they write a letter to the editor, send a bunch of boxes with legal stuff, and get an immediate inquiry? At the time I wrote this original post I probably was still under the inquiry and could not express myself properly on the topic, but now the inquiry is over, the university found no evidence for the accusations of fraud made against me by the drug company, and this editor is probably long gone.]

The American Journal of Psychiatry

1000 Wilson Boulevard, Suite 1825
Arlington, VA 22209-2901
Telephone 703.907.8600
Fax 703.907.1096
E-mail ajp@psych.org

December 19, 2007

To: Thomas J. Lawley, M.D.
    J. Douglas Bremner, M.D.

Editor-in-Chief
Robert Freedman, M.D.

Deputy Editors
David A. Lewis, M.D.
Robert Michels, M.D.
Daniel S. Pine, M.D.
Susan K. Schultz, M.D.
Carol A. Tamminga, M.D.

Editorial Director
Michael D. Roy

Senior Editor/Features Writer
Jane Weaver, E.L.S.

Senior Editors
John J. Guardiano, Ph.D.
Leannah M. Harding, M.S., E.L.S.

Assistant Editors
Lisa Devine
Angela Moore

Production Editor
Julie C. Blair

Senior Graphic Designer
Jason Glance

Editorial Manager
Molly Douglas

Editorial Assistant
Samantha Luck

Administrative Assistant
Kourtney Skinner

Fr: Robert Freedman, M.D.
    Michael D. Roy

cc: Joann MacBeth, J.D., Crowell & Moring

Enclosed is a letter that accompanied a box of materials we received from Colleen M. Hennessey at Peabody & Arnold, LLP, the firm representing Hoffman La Roche in the trial at which an article published in the May 2005 issue of The American Journal of Psychiatry was called into question.

In the letter they point to specific points brought up in testimony that suggests the Journal should conduct an investigation.

Since we have already requested that an inquiry be conducted with regard to this study, we are forwarding the letter to ensure that the results of the investigation have addressed these points.

We had previously sent you the court transcript of the judge's decision that first prompted our request for the inquiry. Throughout the letter, Ms. Hennessey refers to sections of the court transcripts of the hearings. These were enclosed in the box of materials sent to our offices. Since the proceedings cover 9 court sessions over 5 days of testimony, we are now in possession of over 1,300 pages.

We are logistically unable to copy all of these pages and send to each of you, so if there is one specific designee to whom these materials should be sent, please forward the name and mailing address of that individual to Michael Roy (mroy@psych.org).

Official Journal of the American Psychiatric Association

Pills, Shills, and the Psychiatry Wars

The American Journal of Psychiatry

1000 Wilson Boulevard, Suite 1825
Arlington, VA 22209-2901
Telephone 703.907.8690
Fax 703.907.1096
E-mail ajp@psych.org

We note that Dr. Bremner has already retracted a study published in *Biological Psychiatry*. If your inquiry finds serious errors or omissions in this study, we also request that your inquiry verify the other studies published in *The American Journal of Psychiatry* from Emory University.

We very much appreciate your cooperation in this matter.

Sincerely,

Robert Freedman

Robert Freedman, M.D.
Editor in Chief

Michael D. Roy
Managing Editor

1. Bremner JD, Fani N, Ashraf A, Votaw JR, Brummer ME, Cummins T, Vaccarino V, Goodman MM, Reed L, Siddiq S, Nemeroff CB: Functional brain imaging alterations in acne patients treated with isotretinoin. American Journal of Psychiatry 2005; 162:983-991.

Enclosures:

1. Original article in *The American Journal of Psychiatry* by Bremner et al.

2. Judge Francine A Schott's Ruling, November 8, 2007

3. List of publications in *The American Journal of Psychiatry* by Dr. Bremner

4. Notice of Retraction from *Biological Psychiatry*

cc: J. Douglas Bremner, M.D.

Pills, Shills, and the Psychiatry Wars

Chapter 72: ADHD Drugs Not Better Than Psychotherapy After Three Years

(Originally posted March 30, 2009, in *Drug Safety & Health News*).

This has been knocked around in the blogosphere after an article in *The Washington Post*[169] publicized this week's study results, however I thought I would give the study[170] my usual thorough going over. The ongoing NIH funded Multi-site Multimodality Treatment of Attention Deficit Hyperactivity Disorder (MTA) study (updated in an article this week in the *Journal of the American Academy of Child & Adolescent Psychiatry*) showed that treatment with the stimulant medication Ritalin (methylphenidate) wasn't any better than behavioral treatment after three years. As the parent of a child diagnosed with ADD who struggled for two years trying to cope on our own, going through hell for another two years with medications and their nightmare side effects (described in my book using a pseudonym) I sure would have liked to have known about these results (he's off meds now and doing well), or in fact that behavioral treatment has been shown to be effective[171] (I honestly didn't know until today-- blame myself). Thanks, National Institute of Health (NIH), for issuing a press release when these study results first came out in 2007[172] and glossing over the results by describing a "remarkable improvement in all groups" while euphemistically describing the result that Ritalin knocked an inch off of kids growth by stating that kids treated with behavioral treatment were "somewhat larger."

Humph.

Anyhoo back to the study. Children received either Ritalin or behavioral treatment or a combination of both, or received "regular care" or community care, administered in a placebo controlled randomized study design. Behavioral treatment involved 27 group parent sessions, 8 individual parent sessions, an eight-week summer treatment program, 12 weeks of classroom behavioral therapy, and 10 teacher consultation sessions. At one year Ritalin or combination worked better than behavioral treatment, a result that was much trumpeted by the study authors. After one year patients were followed for another two years without controlled treatment. Although some kids went off drugs and some originally treated with behavioral therapy went on drugs, at the two and three year followup there were still more kids on medication in the original medication treated group than in the behavioral therapy group.

The result? Children who were originally treated with medication did no better than those treated originally with behavioral treatment at three years after the original start of treatment.

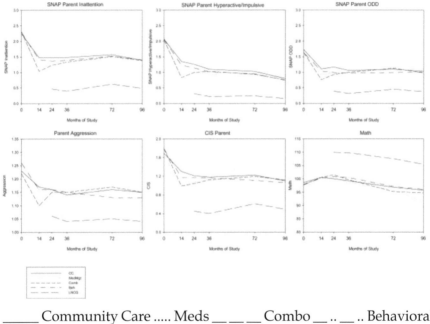

_____ Community Care ..... Meds __ __ __ Combo __ .. __ .. Behavioral Rx ____ ___ ___ LCNG= Normal

What's interesting about this study that was not noticed in the press coverage is that based on the study results it isn't clear if any kind of treatment is better than just leaving the kids alone for a couple of years. It's hard to know though because the "community care" group also got treated with various medications and psychotherapies, but we really don't know which ones.

Another thing is that by doing a press release it put a positive spin on the results that borderlines on fraud. Back in 2007 the authors wrote that there was a "remarkable improvement in all the treatment groups" which glossed over the fact that the study showed that medications were not better than behavioral treatment after three years. Even now when one of the study authors, William E. Pelhem, M.D., stated the obvious conclusion that medications are no different than behavioral treatment after three years, he was accused by co-author, Peter S. Jensen, M.D., of being "biased against medications." Here is a quote of Dr. Jensen, read and make your own judgment:

> Jensen said Pelham was the only member of the team of researchers who took away "the silly message" that the study raised questions about the long-term utility of drugs.

Back in 2007 in the NIH press release Jensen made the following absurd comment:

> Our results suggest that medication can make a long-term difference for some children if it's continued with optimal intensity, and not started or added too late in a child's clinical course.

What's with these guys, anyway?

I say why does *The Washington Post* feel the need to get expert opinions? Look at the graph and decide for yourself. There is NO DIFFERENCE.

That said this study was a really goofy study design, one year of randomized treatment followed by two years of letting people drift. The only explanation for how they came up with such a goofy study design is that they were going with Harvard's Joseph Biederman's pronouncements that ADHD is a chronic condition which never gets better (which obviously isn't true. I had to bite my lip the other day when our pediatrician sat there and told us that ADHD was a permanent condition and if our son was doing well now off meds that he would probably need to take meds again next year if his class wasn't as interesting. Grrr.) and that treatment gains at one year

262

would hold up at three years (which they didn't). They must have been surprised at the findings and came up with all kinds of goofy explanations and press releases and stuff and then were relieved when they got away with it. I know that if I had read the paper in 2007 (I didn't) I wouldn't have let them get away with that. I don't know if this study tells us that much, other than that giving your kids Ritalin at age 9 for a year won't make a difference when he's 12 over doing behavioral treatment. Looking at this data I was starting to wonder if behavioral treatment was worth the effort or whether kids just got better on their own, however I found this study by Pelham et al 2005[173] that showed that intensive behavioral treatments were better than doing nothing. I just wish someone had told me that such treatments were useful. I guess that's what I get for putting my faith in pediatricians and child psychiatrists. It's all drugs, drugs, drugs.

Another thing is that letting authors say things like "all treatment groups showed a remarkable improvement" rather than "the medication treatment group was no better than the other groups" made me wonder who was responsible for allowing this rot to get published. The current study, the 2007 study, and the infamous Study 329 of SSRIs in kids, all share in common publication in the *Journal of the American Academy of Child & Adolescent Psychiatry*.

Maybe we should compare Ritalin to treatment with a wet noodle. Hiyah!

Pay attention in class!

[Update] William Pelham, Ph.D., one of the original study authors of the MTA, subsequently published a study that showed that children with ADHD who initially get behavioral training of parents for do better than children who are started on medications alone.[174] The logic is that teaching cognitive strategies early on, followed by medication intervention, rather than relying on medications alone brings more benefit in the long run.

Chapter 73: Drug Makers Draw Up Doctors Hit List

(Originally posted March 31, 2009, in *Drug Safety and Health News*)

Well, we knew it was the case all along but this week there are emails released as part of Vioxx (rofecoxib) litigation in Australia against the drug company Merck related to Vioxx-induced heart attacks, that show that Merck drew up a "hit list" of doctors in academia whose opinions about Vioxx were negative in order to "neutralize" or "discredit" them (their words, not mine). One of the emails stated:

> *We may need to seek them out and destroy them where they live.*

In other words, use influence and intimidation to block their promotion, remove their research funding, or threaten their universities with such tactics. Some doctors get death threats and letters are sent to their deans, or their deans get phone calls. As I have written previously, Hoffmann La Roche Pharmaceuticals didn't like my opinion about their acne drug Accutane and depression and went to great lengths to discredit me. One attorney who came onto the scene late said it was a "cautionary tale" and another one said that they did that in order to make an example, so that no one in the future would say negative things about their drugs.

So, what you have is a picture where drug companies shell out hundreds of thousands of dollars to key academic physician leaders to buy their good will, and those whom they can't buy off they try to destroy.

Hat tip to Marilyn Mann.

[update: video of "V-squad" training video of superheroes used to train Vioxx sales team posted here.][175]

[Update: Roche also had a training video for drug reps called "Dodge Ball." It showed reps throwing a ball around with the subtitle "Someone asks you a question about Accutane and depression? Dodge it!"]

Chapter 74: Before You See That Psychiatrist

(Originally posted April 1, 2009, in *Drug News and Health Safety*).

It's not bad enough that if you go see a psychiatrist that they may give you medications of questionable efficacy that may be complicated by making it hard for you to get off your couch and other side effects. But as I was discussing at lunch the other day with Charles Whitfield, M.D., friend and fellow Atlanta M.D. author and author of *The Truth About Mental Illness* and other books like *Healing the Inner Child,* psychotherapy can be helpful but can also be a double-edged sword. That made me think about my long-term psychotherapy supervision as a Yale psychiatry resident. The supervisors were great, I followed a patient for several years and they met with me (two of them) for an hour a week, they were both with the New England Psychoanalytical Institute, which was affiliated with Yale, and both had offices on Trumbull Street in New Haven, CT, which was "therapy row."

Therapy Row, Trumbull St, in New Haven CT.

Their names were Charles Gardner, M.D., and Ira Levine, M.D. After I graduated I subletted Charlie Gardner's office for my own small private practice for a while. Then I moved my practice to my house.

My five-year-old daughter liked to talk to the borderline-strippers with total body tattoos in the waiting room. Oddly they seemed to be at a similar level of psychological development.

When I interviewed at Emory Steven Levy M.D., who was (is) a psychoanalyst, kind of eyed me funny, as I was a researcher who was primarily focused on brain imaging studies in PTSD. He is now the acting chair of psychiatry at Emory. How ironic. He probably doesn't know that I was born at the Menninger Clinic in Topeka KS, where my father was a psychiatry resident and whose mentor was the famous American psychoanalyst Karl Menninger, M.D. One of his jobs was entertaining visitors to the Menninger Clinic, who included Aldous Huxley, the author of the book *Brave New World*, who had dinner at our house.

Aldous Huxley

Anyhoo Charlie Gardner gave me a paper by a psychiatrist and analyst named Robert Langs, M.D. He wrote several books including

Rating Your Psychotherapist[176] which I went back and repurchased. The gist of these books is that there are certain principles that characterize good therapists, including the fact that they start and end on time. Langs discussed the "frame" of therapy as something almost religious, which at the time I thought sounded nuts, but with time I came to appreciate as being very important. He makes these points about what is required for a good therapy:

- o   A single set fee.
- o   A single, set location.
- o   A set time for and length of sessions
- o   A soundproof office
- o   The rule of free association
- o   The therapist limited to neutral interventions (i.e., not from personal needs of therapist)
- o   The relative anonymity of the therapist (no self-revelation or opinions, work limited to the material from the patient)
- o   Total privacy
- o   Total confidentiality

I don't think this list is unreasonable. And I don't think it is unreasonable to request that someone you are paying money to should abide by these rules if that is what you want. And yes dreams are important, in spite of what the Shrink Rap bloggers think,[177] and I recommend this book, *Decoding Your Dreams*. He recommends free association from the elements of the dream, identifying the day's event that triggered the dream, and not writing it down or talking about it with others (to let the dream continue to grow in meaning).

Unfortunately, the current generation of psychiatrists was trained by the pharma-bio consortium, and doesn't always take dreams and therapy seriously, but the "New Psychiatry" is on the way (stay tuned).

Chapter 75: Live Blogging from Messina, Italy: Pills and Politics

(Originally posted April 7, 2009, in *Drug News and Health Safety*).

I previously wrote in my book *Before You Take That Pill* about the story of my Sicilian mother-in-law who was put on the alpha adrenergic blocker drug Cardura (doxazosin) for hypertension in spite of the fact that in the NIH-sponsored ALLHAT study over a decade ago the group that was taking the alpha blockers was stopped early because the risk of death was increased compared to the group that was taking a diuretic and a beta blocker, and the group taking calcium channel blockers and angiotensin converting enzyme (ACE) inhibitors.[178] It really irks me when physicians do not use evidence-based medicine but just use whatever they are used to. The logic might be that it has been useful in lowering blood pressure in their other patients, and they don't know or care what effect it has on heart attacks, strokes, and mortality, which is what the rest of us little guys care about.

Dylan and Sabina Bremner with their uncle Nino in Messina, Italy

Don't get me started on my father-in-law, who is becoming increasingly deaf at the age of 89, and who isn't as perky as he used to be, and who 'stopped working', therefore his Italian physician has brilliantly put him on several different psychotropic medications for a "pochino depression."

Is that in the DSM? Should that be under consideration for the DSM Shadow Team?

Anyhoo now my brother-in-law has now been prescribed Cardura for high blood pressure (what is it with these Italian physicians and Cardura? They must be giving out some really great pens or maybe something even better. Hmmm...). He told his physician about what I had written about Cardura and his physician's response was:

> *Those American physicians make a lot of mistakes.*

Humph.

Another news item from Italy this week is related to the earthquake that flattened much of the city of Aquila and the region of Molise. BTW thanks guys who were asking about me. The Italians fearless leader, Silvio Berlusconi, after seeing the 28,000 people who were living in tents, made the brilliant comment:

> *They should try and enjoy themselves and pretend they
> are camping.*

This from the guy who made a former topless model and "showgirl" a member of his cabinet, a woman he said he would marry instantly if he wasn't already married. Which led to his wife demanding a public apology in one of his newspapers. Which he gave. Oh, he also said Obama had a "suntan."

Silvio Berlusconi relaxing with cabinet member Mara Carfagna.

I swear I am not making this stuff up.

The interesting thing about his 'camping' comment is that although this idiotic comment made the front page of *The London Times*, there was not one word in the Italian papers. Maybe that is because he owns all three major TV networks and had influence over the newspapers and other media outlets as well. You know how Jon Stewart likes to lampoon government leaders? The last comedian to make fun of Berlusconi on TV ended her show with "see you next week... maybe." That was back in 2003 and we haven't seen her since. Berlusconi's government replied that the *Times* should have written about how the earthquake victims clapped for Berlusconi. Maybe we should get Sarah Palin to clap into the microphone with them.

Anyhoo, since presumably the majority of Italians voted for this clown (three times??), and since he is right wing presumably a majority of physicians, who are they to say that we make 'a lot of mistakes'?

Now read online "Prescription Medications for the Treatment of Hypertension."[179]

Pills, Shills, and the Psychiatry Wars

[Update] Silvio Berlusconi has since died.

Chapter 76: Live Blogging from Verbania, Italy: Aspartame and Bees and Pass the Diet Coke, Please

(Originally posted April 12, 2009, in *Drug News and Health Safety*).

Today we visited our daughter who is an exchange student in Verbania, Italy, on the northern shore of Lake Maggiore, in the region of Piemonte. Her host father is a bee cultivator and proprietor of a small company that produces honey and wax. He travels up into the Italian Alps every day to tend to their bees.

Verbania, Italy

He told us that the population of bees is declining worldwide due to various factors such as pesticides in the environment. But what is a weird twist is that a substance that is in diet coke, aspartame, may actually help out the bees. Aspartame is added to diet coke as a substitute for sugar. Many Americans drink gallons of this stuff.

Things go better with Coke. That is, if you are a bee.

I'm not sure about the rest of us.

A video on YouTube describes how a man feels like aspartame was responsible for the death of his wife, caused by drinking too much diet Coke.[180]

You see the bees have been suffering from a kind of pest that interferes with their life cycle. This has had a negative effect on the production of honey. They found that when they took a bunch of diet coke and put it out in the sun for a few days, the aspartame in the diet coke underwent a chemical reaction. When given to the bees, it killed the pests that afflicted them.

This might be good news for the bees. But for those of us who drink diet coke?

The FDA has set the Acceptable Dietary Intake (ADI) of Aspartame at 50 mg/kg per day. This is equivalent to 21 cans of diet coke per day. Our European friends might think that this is impossible. But have they ever been to Dallas? And seen a super slurpy special first-hand?

The effects of aspartame on health continue to be controversial. And this is made worse by allegations of conflicts of interest amongst those experts who have opined on the topic. The continuing purchase of our medical experts does not leave room for confidence amongst consumers about these so-called expert opinions. So, they have no one to blame but themselves if no one believes them.

Hat tip to brother Steve Bremner for the Aspartame Youtube video link.

Chapter 77: Live Blogging from Bronte, Italy: Homeopathy

(Originally posted April 14, 2009, in *Drug Safety & Health News*).

Earlier this week my daughter's host father in Verbania IT told us that he was going through a nervous phase when he was having trouble sleeping (haven't we all been through one of those?) when he went to his homeopathic physician. Apparently homeopathic medicine is a big deal these days in Europe, especially in places like the far North of Italy, Switzerland, and Germany. It hasn't caught on really big yet in the US as far as I can tell.

Anyhoo the idea is that small doses of medicines can boost the response to disease and help the body overcome the disease process. I am reminded of the 'spiritual healer' Edgar Cayce whom I have written about on this site who said that he borrowed from allopathic, homeopathic, and osteopathic medicine when he went into a trance and effected diagnosis and cure.

I know nothing about the principles behind osteopathic medicine, although it seems from the osteopathic physicians, I have run across they are effectively doing something pretty similar to what us 'allopathic' physicians are doing.

This week we traveled to Bronte (Sicily) IT to visit the family of a boy whom we are going to host next year as an exchange student in Atlanta.

Bronte, Italy. They were carrying some kind of statue or something. Not sure why.

Relating to homeopathic medicine, I had the following (translated) conversation with the father of the boy.

Should I take an aspirin?

No.

But won't it prevent a heart attack?

It might, but it will also increase your risk of stomach bleeding.

What about homeopathic medicine?

If you take nothing, nothing will happen.

That is pretty much my opinion, but of course we had to do a thorough investigation of the topic, which had to wait until I was done stuffing myself with cannolis and had access to the internet.

Chapter 78: CHADD CEO Offers Lame Response Regarding ADHD Study

(Originally posted April 16, 2009, in *Drug Safety & Health News*).

E. Clarke Ross, CEO of the patient advocate organization Children and Adults with Adult Deficit/Hyperactivity Disorder (CHADD), wrote a rather lame response to a criticism today in a *USA Today* editorial regarding the Multimodal Treatment Study for Attention Deficit/Hyperactivity Study (MTA) of Ritalin versus psychotherapy for the treatment of childhood ADHD, which as I previously wrote on this site did not show that Ritalin was more effective than psychotherapy after three years.

USA Today appropriately points out that maybe parents, doctors, and especially, teachers, shouldn't be rushing to medicate kids who space out in class when they don't fully appreciate the potential side effects, and when they, well, basically stop working after a couple of years.

The fraught conflicts of interest of CHADD have been pointed out in the book *Selling Sickness* by Ray Moynihan and his co-author,[181] and I recommend it to add to your pile of recent books documenting how the pharmaceutical industry has corrupted academic medicine (willingly on their part! Come on in guys the waters fine!) and the American medical system.

Ross writes:

It would be a mistake for parents to use the latest data
from the MTA study as a reason to retreat from using
proven treatments, including medication and
structured behavioral interventions, for the disorder.

I mean come on, buddy. The MTA study was not designed to show that all treatments work well. It was designed to compare medication to behavioral treatment and treatment as usual. The study findings were that after three years medications were not better than either of the other two approaches.

I am a psychiatrist with a son who was diagnosed with ADD and treated with Ritalin. I never heard that there were useful behavioral treatments until... last week. If I got nothing but meds meds meds, I am sure that most other people got the same.

Also, some of Mr. Ross' arguments are at best lame and at worse false. He states that the follow-up was "after the end of the study." What he means is that it was after the double-blind phase of the study was over. However as far as we can tell the three-year followup was also "part of the study," not just some afterthought like he implies.

He also makes the argument that "lack of access to health care" might explain the lack of a difference between groups. However, they measured how many kids were taking stimulants at three years, and 3/4 of the group originally treated with stimulants were still on them, while less than half of the psychotherapy treated group were, so this argument doesn't wash.

Recently Senator Charles Grassley (R-Iowa) has recommended another patient advocacy group, the National Association of the Mentally Ill (NAMI) to disclose payments from pharmaceutical companies. I used to be on the Scientific Advisory Board of a patient advocacy group in the area of anxiety disorders, and I asked them how much of their funding came from drugs companies. I never got a clear answer, so I sort of faded away from that group.

Patient advocacy groups and organizations like the American Heart Association (AHA) and the Osteoporosis Foundation of America are heavily funded by drug companies, and their "screen and identify" programs fit in with the drug companies' agenda to expand their markets to the worried well, as well as providing a convenient front. It is time to take a careful look at these organizations and determine if they are doing more harm than good.

[Update] I've had a lot more experience prescribing stimulants for adults with attentional problems and I am a lot more positive about their efficacy than I was back then.

Chapter 79: Consciousness and Identity: Live Blogging from Dubrovnik, Croatia

(Originally posted April 19, 2009, in *Drug Safety & Health News*).

This week the travelling blog team moves to Dubrovnik, Croatia, for the Sixth Annual Mind and Brain Conference, where I gave a talk about "PTSD and Brain Plasticity."

Dubrovnik, Croatia

One of the main themes of the conference was neurofeedback, the idea that you can train people to alter their brain waves by hooking them up to an EEG machine and then offering them "points" when they get their brain waves to move in the desired direction. One of the presenters, Professor John Gruzelier of Goldsmith College, U. of London, talked about how he had trained musicians to move their brain waves into the alpha/theta range (put simply, the electrical activity of the brain was moving in large slow waves instead of rapid choppy waves) which helped them perform better in their musical performances. How do they do this? By listening to tapes of waves crashing on the beach. Actually, as we were listening to this lecture the windows of the room were open and you could hear... yes, the waves crashing on the beach right outside. If this all seems rather strange... it is. I didn't really understand it myself and asked some questions about it, to which I was referred to the fact that people being trained in this suddenly say that they "get it" and can make

281

their brain waves do the things that the trainers want them to do. Hmmm...

At the coffee break we discussed the theory of the schizophrenic mother, one of the carcasses in the dust bin of psychiatric theory that originated from the Yale University School of Medicine Department of Psychiatry, where I was trained. There were two psychiatrists there named Teddy Lidz and Stephen Fleck who had come up the theory years ago that mothers drove their children crazy, which they published in their book Schizophrenia and the Family.[182] Fleck interviewed me for the psychiatry residency back in 1986 and even then he was extremely old. He used to sit outside of the Connecticut Mental Health Center on the sidewalk in his white coat, smoking a cigarette. He would do case conferences but was so deaf that he couldn't hear anything, but that didn't seem to matter anyway. When I was a resident, someone presented at Grand Rounds at Yale about the genetics of schizophrenia, and Lidz and Fleck stood up and started shouting about how it wasn't just a genetic disorder. Maybe they weren't so crazy after all. Hmm...

There was a Croatian at the conference who was a graduate student in physics who told me at dinner about their research trying to teach violent people how to lower their brain blood flow. They hook violent prisoners up to a functional magnetic resonance imaging machine and then give them "points" when they can get their own insula blood flow to go down. I guess the idea is that the insula is involved in violent behavior, and they are trying to train their brains to be more docile. It all seems a little like ClockWork Orange to me, and I don't think something like that would ever get passed by our investigational review board, but whatever. It doesn't seem like they are able to retain their learned ability to change their brain function anyway. Why not just teach them to meditate? Or give them a Snickers bar?

This new fMRI technology is really great.

I read in the newspaper about a French-Jewish psychiatrist named Boris Cyrulnik who just wrote a book called *Resilience*.[183] Big deal, I thought, everyone talks about that stuff these days. Anyhoo, I read a little more of the article and it said that he was a French Jew whose parents were killed in the Holocaust when he was 7, but that he had managed to survive, largely on his own, and was eventually adopted by someone at the age of 10. Growing up in France, Cyrulnik felt that he couldn't talk to anyone about his parents, especially in the climate of De Gaulist politics and everyone pretending like the French were all a bunch of freedom fighters or something, and he thought that no one wanted to hear about his parents or his experiences. He said that he felt monstrous, and only after growing up and learning to talk about his experiences did he overcome that. He used his own experiences to go on and help other children with a range of other traumatic experiences. Anyhoo, as I have written about on this site my mother died when I was four and a half years old, and afterward I had just that feeling, of being monstrous, and trying to hide that fact from other people, which made me act artificial. I have been wondering lately why the fact that my mother died should be associated with feeling like I was bad? Anyhoo I was talking about it at the meeting with my friend and fellow PTSD researcher, Israel Liberzon, M.D., from the Department of Psychiatry at the University of Michigan, who gave a talk about neuroimaging of PTSD, and he told me that children attribute causes to things, so that if my mother died my childish brain must have decided that it was because of something that I did. And frankly there was no one around to tell me otherwise. Thinking about it I can see that at the age of five I would not be able to see the event of my mother's death as a random fluke that I personally had nothing to do with. And those deep emotions can stay with us for a long time, and it takes a while to ferret them out and find their sources.

Update: see here for more discussion on schizophrenogenic mothers and the effects of early experience, mothers, etc. on mental health.

Chapter 80: Whatever Happened to Pharma Giles?

(Originally posted in *Drug Safety and Health News,* April 21, 2009).

Pharma Giles was a hilarious blog that spoofed the pharmaceutical industry and was a frequent commentator on the (now also defunct) website pharmalot.com. He was a pioneer in the creative use of Photoshop to poke fun and created a fake pharmaceutical company on the internet. When I first clicked on the link to his name from one of his comments and arrived at his site, I wondered… who is this guy? But then when he disappeared it seemed obvious, he must have been a pharma insider who got nabbed by his employer and was forced by their lawyers to take it all down and sign an agreement of secrecy. Which has been pretty effective since no one knows who he is.

So sometime last year Pharma Giles suddenly disappeared from the internet and took down all of his archived posts. That made some of us wonder…

What ever happened to Pharma Giles?

It's like you grew up with a bunch of Armenians, and suddenly they disappeared, and everyone tells you that they never existed.

I came across a reference to Pharma Giles in another blog and started googling him. Someone had preserved his Children's Guide to Modern Medicine which I found here.

If anyone has any more of the old material send it my way.

Chapter 81: Live Blogging from Neuroscience Lecture: Neurobiology of Social Bonds

(Originally posted in *Drug Safety & Health News,* April 23, 2009).

I am sitting in a lecture by Larry Young, Ph.D., of the Yerkes Regional Primate Center here in Atlanta, GA. His research is on the neurobiology of social bonds. Since many of the readers of the *Drug Safety and Health News* often wonder about how things that happened in early childhood affect how things go in later life, I thought this would be of interest.

He studies an animal called the prairie vole (*Microtus ochragaster*), which is unusual amongst mammals for forming life-long mating bonds, like humans (well, sometimes). Interestingly, the meadow vole (*Microtus montanus*), a critter I studied as a med student that lives in the mountain meadows in the West, is genetically very similar to the prairie vole, differing only in having fewer brain receptors for the neuropeptide's oxytocin and vasopressin.

The meadow vole spends about half its time cuddling with its mate.

Don't forget to take out the garbage, honey. (Source: Larry Young, Ph.D.)

While the meadow vole, and the vast majority of other mammals, mates and then hits the road, spending most of its life alone.

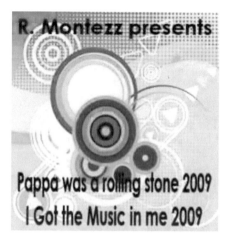

R. Montezz presents

Pappa was a rolling stone 2009
I Got the Music in me 2009

70% of prairie voles who lose a partner never acquire another one. If they are separated from their partners, they show depressed like behavior, like floating in water without struggling, or being immobile in a maze.

Which doesn't mean they never mate with other voles... they just come back to their wives.

All this raises the question... why did monogamy evolve in some animals? I have also been reading about this in a book called _The Well Dressed Ape_, by science writer Hannah Holmes.[184]

Although not all animals are monogamous, all females show maternal behavior. This is regulated by the neuropeptide oxytocin, which induces labor, is released from the brain during nursing to promote milk release and stimulates maternal bonding with pups. For instance, you can inject sheep with oxytocin and that facilitates them becoming dependent on their own lambs via oxytocin. You can also get sheep to bond with foreign lambs using oxytocin injection. Drugs that block oxytocin also block maternal behavior. You can get similar effects for pair bonding of mating voles. These oxytocin receptors are located in parts of the brain involved in emotion, like the striatum and medial prefrontal cortex.

For males, the neuropeptide vasopressin is more prominent. It is involved in aggression, male sexual behavior, territorial behavior, and paternal care. A variation in the vasopressin receptor 1a in humans is associated with a doubling in likelihood to have had a marital crisis in the last year, and to have a partner that is less satisfied, and to be less likely to marry.

Prairie voles raised by a bonded pair (that's right, good ole mom and dad) have more attachment to their partners when they grow up and are more maternal than voles raised by single moms. They also have lower levels of oxytocin.

But don't worry, there is a drug for everything. And it is... you guessed it! Oxytocin in a nasal spray called <u>Liquid Trust</u>! Their claim?

> *Liquid Trust "Enhanced" has been specially designed to give a boost to the dating and relationship area of your life. This upgraded formula still contains the same great Oxytocin formula, but now includes the powerful pheromones Androstenone and Androsterone.*

So, if you don't feel ridiculous spraying this up your date's nose, or your cheating husband, here you go.

Liquid Trust

Postscript

Please go to my author page on amazon and write a review. They help authors a lot, even if brief!

This book is part of a series, Pimps, Whores and Chiggers. The first book was Pimps, Whores, and Chiggers: Musings from the Drug Safety and Health News Blog: The Corrupting Influence of Big Pharma. The next book is Healthcare Politics, which covers my writings during the Obama period and the attempt to fix our broken healthcare system, which I find is still relevant today since nothing is, well, fixed. It also includes posts on other relevant medical topics of the day as well as my usual personal anecdotes. Enjoy!

Praise for 'Pimps, Whores and Chiggers'

The mainstream media... are flailing and failing. The usual reason given is declining readership and ad revenue, but perhaps the real decline is in their relevancy, insight and truthfulness... In general, if you want to get a skeptical, cogently contextualized view of an issue, you have to go online and read blogs like *Drug Safety & Health News* blog by Dr. Douglas Bremner, an exceedingly rare voice of skepticism arrayed against the advertising and lobbying might of the multi-billion-dollar pharmaceutical industry. Charles Hugh Smith, blogger at oftwominds.com writing in his post, "Mainstream Media: Master of the Obvious, Clueless Commentary".

Index

Abilify. *See* aripiprazole
ACA. *See* Affordable Care Act
Accutane. *See* isotretinoin
acne, 9, 16, 31, 32, 39, 98, 99, 100, 152, 182, 248, 249, 255, 265, 299
ACNP. *See* American College of Neuropsychopharmacology
Adderall. *See* amphetamine salts
ADHD. *See* Attention Deficit Hyperactivity Disorder
Affordable Care Act, 42
akathisia, 44, 45
Alabama, 23, 236
alendronate, 172
Alzheimer's Disease, 70
Ambien. *See* zolpidem
American Association for Justice, 48
American College of Neuropsychopharmacology, 88, 90, 103, 108, 117, 236
American Medical Association, 32, 234
American Psychiatric Association, 103, 105, 236
American Psychosomatic Society, 189, 195
amphetamine salts, 132
Angell, Marcia, 138
antidepressants, 11, 45, 69, 88, 89, 108, 109, 116, 129, 176, 179, 204, 205
antioxidants, 24, 299
aripiprazole, 44
aspartame, 273, 274
aspirin, 24, 25, 65, 66, 197, 198, 277, 299
AstraZeneca, 58, 174, 202
atorvastatin, 80
atrial fibrillation, 172, 199
Attention Deficit Hyperactivity Disorder, 67, 260
Avelox. *See* moxifloxacin
Bass, Alison, 76

Bibliography

[1] Harris, Gardiner: "Top Psychiatrist Didn't Report Drug Makers' Pay," *The New York Times,* Oct. 3, 2008. Retrieved July 14, 2023, from: https://www.nytimes.com/2008/10/04/health/policy/04drug.html.

[2] Bremner, Doug: "Exercise Better Than Drugs for Depression." *Doug Bremner Website* Retrieved Aug 19, 2023, from: https://www.dougbremner.com/topics/depression/exercise-better-than-drugs-for-depression.html.

[3] Belch, J. et al: The prevention of progression of arterial disease and diabetes (POPADAD) trial: factorial randomised placebo-controlled trial of aspirin and antioxidants in patients with diabetes and asymptomatic peripheral arterial disease," *BMJ* 2008; 337: a1840 doi: https://doi.org/10.1136/bmj.a1840 (Published 16 October 2008) Retrieved July 14, 2023, from: https://www.bmj.com/content/337/bmj.a1840.full.

[4] Staff: "Diabetes aspirin use questioned." *BBC News* (17 October 2008) Retrieved Aug 19, 2023, from: http://news.bbc.co.uk/2/hi/health/7673587.stm.

[5] Bremner, Doug: Probiotics for Bowel Conditions: Is There Any Evidence They Are Helpful?" *Doug Bremner Personal Website* Retrieved Aug 23, 2023, from: https://www.dougbremner.com/topics/antibiotics/probiotics.html.

[6] Giezen TJ, Mantel-Teeuwisse AK, Straus SMJM, et al: Safety-related regulatory actions for biologicals approved in the United States and the European Union. *JAMA* 2008 Oct 22;300(16):1887-96. doi: 10.1001/jama.300.16.1887. PMID: 18940975 DOI: 10.1001/jama.300.16.1887 Retrieved Aug 19, 2023, from: https://pubmed.ncbi.nlm.nih.gov/18940975/.

[7] DeAngelis CD, Fontanarosa PB: Prescription Drugs, Products Liability, and Preemption of Tort Litigation. *JAMA.* 2008;300(16):1939-1941. doi:10.1001/jama.2008.513. Retrieved Aug 19, 2023, from: https://jamanetwork-com.proxy.library.emory.edu/journals/jama/fullarticle/182769.

[8] Peck GL, Olsen TG, Yoder FW, et al. Prolonged remissions of cystic and conglobate acne with 13-cis-retinoic acid. *The New England Journal of Medicine.* 1979; 300:329-333.

9 Yoder FW. Isotretinoin: A word of caution. *J Am Med Assoc.* 1983;249(3):350-351. Retrieved Aug 19, 2023, from: https://jamanetwork.com/journals/jama/article-abstract/382151.
10 McCoy K. Drug Maker rebuffed call to monitor users. *USA Today* (December 7, 2004): 1-2.
11 Tinari, Serena: *Morire per la pelle* (Skin to Die For). *Radio Svizzero Italiano* (2008) Retrieved Aug 19, 2023, from: https://www.youtube.com/watch?v=lBF0eUMCyGA.
12 Ross JS, Nazem AG, Lurie P, et al: Updated Estimates of Pharmaceutical Company Payments to Physicians in Vermont. *JAMA* 2008;300(17):1998-2000. doi:10.1001/jama.2008.560 Retrieved Aug 5, 2023, from: https://jamanetwork.com/journals/jama/fullarticle/182823.
13 Berman RM, Marcus RN, Swanink R, et al: The efficacy and safety of aripiprazole as adjunctive therapy in major depressive disorder: a multicenter, randomized, double-blind, placebo-controlled study. *J Clin Psychiatry* 2007 Jun;68(6):843-53. doi: 10.4088/jcp.v68n0604. Retrieved July 18, 2023, from: https://www.psychiatrist.com/jcp/depression/efficacy-safety-aripiprazole-adjunctive-therapy-major/.
14 Marcus RN, McQuade RD, Carson WH, et al: The Efficacy and Safety of Aripiprazole as Adjunctive Therapy in Major Depressive Disorder: A Second Multicenter, Randomized, Double-Blind, Placebo-Controlled Study. *Journal of Clinical Psychopharmacology* 2008; (2):156-165. doi: 10.1097/JCP.0b013e31816774f9. Retrieved July 18, 2023, from: https://journals.lww.com/psychopharmacology/pages/articleviewer.aspx?year=2008&issue=04000&article=00005&type=abstract.
15 Bremner, Doug: "Is Chromium Useful for the Treatment of Diabetes?" *Doug Bremner Personal Website* Accessed Sep 1, 2023, from: https://www.dougbremner.com/topics/diabetes/is-chromium-useful-for-the-treatment-of-diabetes.html.
16 Mencimer, Stephanie: "Daniel Troy's Poison Pill." *Mother Jones* (March 7, 2008) Retrieved Aug 7, 2023, from: https://www.motherjones.com/politics/2008/03/daniel-troys-poison-pill/.
17 Bremner, J. Douglas: *Before You Take That Pill: Why the Drug Industry May be Bad for Your Health: Risks and Side Effects You Won't Find on the Label of Commonly Prescribed Medications, Vitamins and Supplements* Penguin/Avery New York, 2008.
18 Lautenbach E; Larosa LA; Kasbekar N; et al: Fluoroquinolone Utilization in the Emergency Departments of Academic Medical Centers Prevalence of, and Risk Factors for, Inappropriate Use.

Arch Intern Med. 2003;163(5):601-605. doi:10.1001/archinte.163.5.601. Retrieved Aug 6, 2023, from: https://jamanetwork.com/journals/jamainternalmedicine/fullarticle/215194.

[19] Kaur K, Raja Fayad R, Arpit Saxena A: Southern Network on Adverse Reactions (SONAR) project, et al: Fluoroquinolone-related neuropsychiatric and mitochondrial toxicity: a collaborative investigation by scientists and members of a social network. *J Community Support Oncol* 2016 Feb;14(2):54-65. doi: 10.12788/jcso.0167. Retrieved Aug 6, 2023, from: https://www.mdedge.com/hematology-oncology/article/106661/patient-survivor-care/fluoroquinolone-related-neuropsychiatric.

[20] Golomb BA, Koslik HJ, Redd AJ: Fluoroquinolone-induced serious, persistent, multisymptomatic adverse effects. *BMJ Case Rep.* 2015; 2015: bcr2015209821. Published online 2015 Oct 5. doi: 10.1136/bcr-2015-209821. PMCID: PMC4600819. PMID: 26438672. 2 Retrieved Aug 6, 2023, from: https://www.ncbi.nlm.nih.gov/pmc/articles/PMC4600819/.

[21] Golomb BA, Koslik HJ, Redd AJ: Fluoroquinolone-induced serious, persistent, multi-symptom adverse effects. *BMJ Case Rep.* 2015; 2015: bcr2015209821. Published online 2015 Oct 5. doi: 10.1136/bcr-2015-209821. PMCID: PMC4600819. PMID: 26438672. 2 Retrieved Aug 6, 2023, from: https://www.ncbi.nlm.nih.gov/pmc/articles/PMC4600819/.

[22] Bremner, Doug: "Quinolone Antibiotics Can Have Some Nasty Side Effects." *Doug Bremner Personal Website* Retrieved Aug 5, 2023, from: https://www.dougbremner.com/topics/antibiotics/cipro-can-have-some-nasty-side-effects.html.

[23] Ridker PM, Danielson E, Fonseca FAH, et al. Rosuvastatin to Prevent Vascular Events in Men and Women with Elevated C-Reactive Protein. *The New England Journal of Medicine* 2008; 359:2195-2207. Retrieved July 18, 2023, from: https://www.nejm.org/doi/full/10.1056/NEJMoa0807646.

[24] CAPRIE: A randomised, blinded trial of Clopidogrel versus Aspirin in Patients at Risk of Ischaemic Events (CAPRIE). *The Lancet* 1996; 348(9038): 1329-1339. Accessed Oct 1, 2023, from: https://pubmed.ncbi.nlm.nih.gov/8918275/.

[25] Bhatt DL, et al: Clopidogrel and aspirin versus aspirin alone for the prevention of atherothrombotic events." *New England Journal of Medicine* 2006; 354: 1706-1717. Accessed Oct 1, 2023, from: https://pubmed.ncbi.nlm.nih.gov/16531616/.

[26] Chen ZM, COMMIT, et al: Addition of clopidogrel to aspirin in 45,852 patients with acute myocardial infarction: randomised placebo-controlled

trial. *The Lancet* 2006; 366: 1607-1621. Accessed Oct 1, 2023, from: https://pubmed.ncbi.nlm.nih.gov/16271642/.

[27] ATC: Antithrombotic Trialists' Collaboration: Collaborative meta-analysis of randomised trials of antiplatelet therapy for prevention of death, myocardial infarction, and stroke in high-risk patients. *British Medical Journal* 2002; 324: 71-86. Accessed Oct 1, 2023, from: https://pubmed.ncbi.nlm.nih.gov/11786451/.

[28] Diener H-C, Bogousslavsky J, et al: Aspirin and clopidogrel compared with clopidogrel alone after recent ischaemic stroke or transient ischaemic attack in high-risk patients (MATCH): randomised, double-blind, placebo-controlled trial. *The Lancet* 2004; 364: 331-337. Accessed Oct 1, 2023, from: https://pubmed.ncbi.nlm.nih.gov/15276392/.

[29] Chan FKL, Ching JYL, et al: Clopidogrel versus aspirin and esomeprazole to prevent recurrent ulcer bleeding. New England Journal of Medicine 2005; 352(3): 238-244. Accessed Oct 1, 2023, from: https://pubmed.ncbi.nlm.nih.gov/15659723/.

[30] Chan FKL, Ching JYL, et al: Clopidogrel versus aspirin and esomeprazole to prevent recurrent ulcer bleeding. *New England Journal of Medicine* 2005; 352(3): 238-244. Accessed Oct 1, 2023, from: https://pubmed.ncbi.nlm.nih.gov/15659723/.

[31] Harris, Gardiner: "Use of Antipsychotics in Children is Criticized." *The New York Times* (Nov. 18, 2008) Retrieved Aug 21, 2023, from: https://www.nytimes.com/2008/11/19/health/policy/19fda.html?_r=2%E2%80%99hp%E2%80%99oref=slogin.

[32] Harris, Gardiner: "Radio Host Has Drug Company Ties." *The New York Times* (Nov. 21, 2008) Retrieved Aug 21, 223, from: https://www.nytimes.com/2008/11/22/health/22radio.html?_r=1&scp=1&sq=fred%20goodwin%20npr&st=cse.

[33] Olshansky JS, Passaro DJ, Hershow RC, et al: A potential decline in life expectancy in the United States in the 21st Century. *N Engl J Med.* 2005; 352(11):1138-1145. Retrieved July 18, 2023, from: https://www.nejm.org/doi/full/10.1056/NEJMsr043743.

[34] Bremner, Doug: "Do Changes in Diet or Lifestyle Prevent or Treat Diabetes?" *Doug Bremner Personal Website* Accessed Sep 1, 2023, from: https://www.dougbremner.com/topics/diabetes/do-changes-in-diet-prevent-diabetes.html.

[35] Bremner, Doug: "Medication Treatment of Irritable Bowel Syndrome." *Doug Bremner Personal Website* Accessed Sep 1, 2023, from: https://www.dougbremner.com/topics/GI/medication-treatment-of-ibs.html.

[36] Bass, Alison: *Side Effects: A Prosecutor, a Whistleblower, and a Bestselling Antidepressant on Trial.* Algonquin, 2008. Accessed Oct 1, 2023, from: https://www.amazon.com/Effects-Prosecutor-Whistleblower-Bestselling-Antidepressant/dp/B004C7INKG.

[37] Tilburt JC, Emanuel EJ, Kaptchuk TJ, et al: Prescribing "placebo treatments": results of national survey of US internists and rheumatologists. *BMJ* 2008; 337:a1938. doi: https://doi.org/10.1136/bmj.a1938 (Published 23 October 2008). Retrieved Aug 21, 2023, from: https://www.bmj.com/content/337/bmj.a1938.full.

[38] Dobson, Roger: "Atorvastatin advertising mislead over benefit to women." *BMJ News* (22 October 2008) Retrieved Aug 21, 2023, from: https://www.bmj.com/content/337/bmj.a2209.

[39] Eisenberg T, Wells MT: Statins and Adverse Cardiovascular Events in Moderate-Risk Females: A Statistical and Legal Analysis with Implications for FDA Preemption Claims. *Journal of Empirical Legal Studies* 2008 5(3):507-550. 05 September 2008. doi: 10.1111/j.1740-1461.2008.00132.x. Retrieved Aug 21, 2023, from: https://onlinelibrary.wiley.com/doi/abs/10.1111/j.1740-1461.2008.00132.x.

[40] Bremner, Doug: "Are Calcium and Vitamin D Good For Your Bone Health?" *Doug Bremner Personal Website* Accessed Sep 1, 2023, from: https://www.dougbremner.com/topics/vitamins/are-calcium-and-vitamin-d-good-for-your-bone-health.html.

[41] Levine, Dan, Robin Respaut, Kristina Cooke, Mike Spector and Benjamin Lesser: "A son died, his parents tried to sue: How U.S. courts protect Big Pharma." *Reuters* (June 26, 2023) Retrieved Aug 21, 2023, from: https://www.reuters.com/investigates/special-report/usa-lawsuits-merck-singulair/.

[42] *Americans for Drug and Device Accountability -- Justice in Michigan (ADDA-JIM) Retrieved* Aug 21, 2023, from: http://www.pharmaccountability.org.

[43] Mann 1JJ, Emslie G, Baldessarini RJ, Beardslee W, Fawcett JA, Goodwin FK, Leon AC, Meltzer HY, Ryan ND, Shaffer D, Wagner KD: ACNP Task Force report on SSRIs and suicidal behavior in youth. *Neuropsychopharmacology* 2006 Mar;31(3):473-92. doi: 10.1038/sj.npp.1300958. PMID: 16319919 DOI: 10.1038/sj.npp.1300958. Retrieved Aug 11, 2023, from: https://pubmed.ncbi.nlm.nih.gov/16319919/.

[44] Staff: "Drug firms wine, dine, and pay up for doctors' speeches." *Milwaukee Sentinel-Journal* (Jan 12, 2009) Retrieved Aug 11, 2023, from: https://archive.jsonline.com/features/health/37421114.html/.

[45] Davis SR, Moreau M, Kroll R, for the APHRODITE Study Team, et al: Testosterone for low libido in post-menopausal women not taking estrogen. *N Engl J Med* 2008; 359:2005-2017. November 6, 2008. DOI: 10.1056/NEJMoa0707302. Retrieved Aug 8, 2023, from: https://www.nejm.org/doi/full/10.1056/NEJMoa0707302.

[46] Tamimi RM, Byrne C, Colditz GA, Hankinson SE: Endogenous Hormone Levels, Mammographic Density, and Subsequent Risk of Breast Cancer in Postmenopausal Women. *JNCI: Journal of the National Cancer Institute* 2007; 99(15):1178–1187. doi: 10.1093/jnci/djm062. Retrieved Aug 21, 2023, from: https://academic.oup.com/jnci/article/99/15/1178/1006918.

[47] Maturana MA, Breda V, Lhullier F, Spritzer PM: Relationship between endogenous testosterone and cardiovascular risk in early postmenopausal women.
Metabolism 2008 Jul;57(7):961-5. doi: 10.1016/j.metabol.2008.02.012. PMID: 18555838 DOI: 10.1016/j.metabol.2008.02.012. Retrieved Aug 21, 2023, from: https://pubmed.ncbi.nlm.nih.gov/18555838/.

[48] Bremner, Doug: "Should I Take Testosterone to Boost My Libido?" *Doug Bremner Personal Website* Retrieved Aug 7, 2023, from: https://www.dougbremner.com/topics/sexuality_reproduction/should-i-take-testosterone-to-boost-my-libido.html.

[49] Peck GL, Olsen TG, Yoder FW, et al: Prolonged Remissions of Cystic and Conglobate Acne with 13-cis-Retinoic Acid. *The New England Journal of Medicine.* 1979; 300: 329-333. DOI: 10.1056/NEJM197902153000701 Retrieved July 22, 2023, from: https://www.nejm.org/doi/full/10.1056/NEJM197902153000701.

[50] Gupta MA, Gupta AK, Schork NJ, Ellis CN, Voorhees JJ. Psychiatric aspects of the treatment of mild to moderate facial acne: Some preliminary observations. *Int J Dermatol.* 1990;29(10):719-721. Accessed Oct 1, 2023, from: https://pubmed.ncbi.nlm.nih.gov/2148562/.

[51] McCoy, Kevin: "Drug Maker Rebuffed Call to Monitor Users." *USA Today* (December 7, 2004)., pp. 1-2.

[52] Yoder FW: Isotretinoin: A word of caution. *Journal of the American Medical Association* 1983; 249(3), 350-351. Accessed Oct 1, 2023, from: https://pubmed.ncbi.nlm.nih.gov/6217354/.

[53] Green J, Hutt, P: *Babies, blemishes, and FDA: A history of Accutane regulation in the United States.* Leda. Cambridge, MA. 2002. Accessed Oct 1, 2023, from: https://dash.harvard.edu/bitstream/handle/1/8963867/Green.pdf?sequence=1&isAllowed=y

[54] Green J, Hutt, P: *Babies, blemishes, and FDA: A history of Accutane regulation in the United States.* Leda. Cambridge, MA. 2002. Accessed Oct 1, 2023, from:

https://dash.harvard.edu/bitstream/handle/1/8963867/Green.pdf?sequ
ence=1&isAllowed=y
[55] Jacobs, D. G., Deutsch, N., Brewer, M. (2001). Suicide, depression, and
isotretinoin: Is there a causal link? *Journal of the American Academy of
Dermatology* 2021; 45:S168. Accessed Oct 1, 2023, from:
https://pubmed.ncbi.nlm.nih.gov/11606949/.
[56] Strom, B. L. (Ed.): *Pharmacoepidemiology* (4 ed.). New York: Wiley, 2005.
[57] O'Connell K A, Wilkin J K, Pitts M: Isotretinoin (Accutane) and serious
psychiatric adverse events. *Journal of the American Academy of Dermatology.*
2002; 48(2):306-307. Accessed Oct 1, 2023, from:
https://pubmed.ncbi.nlm.nih.gov/12582415/.
[58] Alcalay J: Myths of isotretinoin therapy in patients with acne: A personal
opinion. *Journal of Drugs in Dermatology* 2024; 3(2):179-182. Accessed Oct 1,
2023: from: https://pubmed.ncbi.nlm.nih.gov/15098974/.
[59] Bremner JD, Shearer KD, McCaffery PJ: Retinoic acid and affective
disorders: the evidence for an association. *The Journal of Clinical Psychiatry*
2012; 73:(1)37-50. Accessed Oct 1, 2023, from:
https://pubmed.ncbi.nlm.nih.gov/2190302.
[60] Bremner JD, McCaffery PJ: The neurobiology of retinoic acid in affective
disorders. *Progress in Neuro-psychopharmacology & Biological Psychiatry* 2008;
32(2):315-331. Accessed Oct 1, 2023, from:
https://www.ncbi.nlm.nih.gov/pmc/articles/PMC2704911/.
[61] Bremner JD: Isotretinoin and neuropsychiatric side effects: Continued
vigilance is needed. *Journal of Affective Disorders Reports* 2021; 6:100230.
Accessed Oct 1, 2023, from:
https://www.sciencedirect.com/science/article/pii/S2666915321001566.
[62] Willman, David: (Jun 23, 2004) "NIH to Curb Its Scientists Ties to Drug
Firms." *The New York Times* Retrieved Aug 1, 2023, from:
https://www.latimes.com/archives/la-xpm-2004-jun-23-na-nih23-
story.html.
[63] Moynihan, Ray: "Key opinion leaders: independent experts or drug
representatives in disguise?"
BMJ 2008; 336 doi: https://doi.org/10.1136/bmj.39575.675787.651
(Published 19 June 2008)
Cite this as: BMJ 2008; 336:1402 Retrieved August 1, 2023, from:
https://www.bmj.com/content/336/7658/1402.full.
[64] Harris, Gardiner: "Top Psychiatrist Didn't Report Drug Makers Pay." *The
New York Times* (Oct 3, 2008) Retrieved Aug 1, 2023, from:
https://www.nytimes.com/2008/10/04/health/policy/04drug.html.

65 Leucht S, Corves C, Arbter D, Engel RR, et al: Second-generation versus first-generation antipsychotic drugs for schizophrenia: a meta-analysis. *Lancet* 2009 Jan 3;373(9657):31-41. doi: 10.1016/S0140-6736(08)61764-X. Epub 2008 Dec 6. PMID: 19058842. Retrieved Aug 21, 2023, from: https://pubmed.ncbi.nlm.nih.gov/19058842/.
66 Brody, Howard: *Hooked: Ethics, the Medical Profession, and the Pharmaceutical Industry* (2006) Rowman & Littlefield. Retrieved Aug 21, 2023, from: http://www.amazon.com/Hooked-Medical-Profesion-Pharmaceutical-Industry/dp/0742552187.
67 Lieberman JA, Stroup TS, McEvoy JP, et al. Effectiveness of antipsychotic drugs in patients with chronic schizophrenia. *The New England Journal of Medicine.* 2005;353(12):1209-1223. Retrieved Aug 21, 2023, from: https://www.nejm.org/doi/full/10.1056/NEJMoa051688.
68 Tyrer P, Kendall T: The spurious advance of antipsychotic drug therapy. *Lancet* 2009; 373(9657):4-5. doi: 10.1016/S0140-6736(08)61765-1. Retrieved Aug 21, 2023, from: http://www.thelancet.com/journals/lancet/article/PIIS0140-6736(08)61765-1/fulltext.
69 Sharav, Vera: "Lancet: Atypicals Antipsychotics—Who 'Beguiled' Doctors?" *Alliance for Human Research Protection* (Jan. 10, 2009).
70 Bremner, Doug: "Should We Be Giving Antipsychotic Drugs to the Elderly?" *Doug Bremner Personal Website* Accessed Sep 1, 2023, from: https://www.dougbremner.com/topics/ad/should-we-be-giving-antipsychotic-drugs-to-the-elderly.html. http://groups.google.com/group/misc.activism.progressive/browse_thread/thread/37fad30387cbf103/b89a524502b3da8b?lnk=raot.71 Armstrong, David: "Medical Journal Nemeroff Steps Down Over Undisclosed Ties." *The Wall Street* Journal (Aug 28, 2006) Retrieved Aug 11, 2023, from: https://www.wsj.com/articles/SB115654102420045878.
72 Bremner JD, Alvarado Ortega R, Campanella C, Nye JA, Davis LL, Fani N and Vaccarino V. Neural correlates of PTSD in women with childhood sexual abuse with and without PTSD and response to paroxetine treatment: A placebo-controlled, double-blind trial. *J Affect Disord Rep.* 2023; 14:100615. Retrieved Sep 18, 2023, from: https://www.sciencedirect.com/science/article/pii/S2666915323001543.
73 Vermetten E, Vythilingam M, Southwick SM, Charney DS, Bremner JD: Long-term treatment with paroxetine increases verbal declarative memory and hippocampal volume in posttraumatic stress disorder. *Biological Psychiatry* 2003; 54:(7):693-702. Retrieved Sep 12, 2023, from: https://pubmed.ncbi.nlm.nih.gov/14512209/.

[74] Carlat, Daniel: "Dr. Drug Rep." *The New York Times* (Nov. 25, 2007) Retrieved Aug 11, 2023, from: https://www.nytimes.com/2007/11/25/magazine/25memoir-t.html?_r=1.

[75] "Drug firms' wine, dine, and pay up for doctors' speeches." *Milwaukee Sentinel-Journal* (Jan 12, 2009) Retrieved Aug 11, 2023, from: https://archive.jsonline.com/features/health/37421114.html/.

[76] Harris, Gardiner: "Top Psychiatrist Didn't Report Drug Makers Pay." *The New York* Times (Oct 3, 2008) Retrieved Aug 1, 2023, from: https://www.nytimes.com/2008/10/04/health/policy/04drug.html.

[77] Brody, Howard: *Hooked: Ethics, the Medical Profession, and the Pharmaceutical Industry* (2006) Rowman & Littlefield.

[78] Walkup JT, Albano AM, Piacentini J, et al: Cognitive behavioral therapy, sertraline, or a combination in childhood anxiety. *N Engl J Med.* 2008 Dec 25;359(26):2753-66. doi: 10.1056/NEJMoa0804633. Epub 2008 Oct 30. Retrieved Aug 5, 2023, from: https://pubmed.ncbi.nlm.nih.gov/18974308/.

[79] Keller MB, Ryan ND, Strober M, et al: Efficacy of paroxetine in the treatment of adolescent major depression: a randomized, controlled trial. *Journal of the American Academy of Child and Adolescent Psychiatry* 2001; 40(7):762–772. doi:10.1097/00004583-200107000-00010 PMID 11437014. Accessed Oct 1, 2023, form: https://www.justice.gov/sites/default/files/opa/legacy/2012/07/02/complaint-ex2.pdf.

[80] Bremner JD, Vaccarino V: Behavior therapy, sertraline, or both in childhood anxiety: Comment. *NEJM* 2009; 360(23): 2476. Retrieved Aug 5, 2023, from: https://pubmed.ncbi.nlm.nih.gov/19504764/.

[81] DPPRG. Reduction in the incidence of type 2 diabetes with lifestyle intervention or metformin. Diabetes Prevention Program Research Group. *The New England Journal of Medicine.* 2002;346(6):393-403.

[82] Bremner, Doug: "A Growing Market for Diabetes." *Doug Bremner Personal Website* Accessed Sep 1, 2023, from: https://www.dougbremner.com/topics/diabetes/a-growing-market-for-diabetes.html.

[83] Mack, John: "FDA DTC Hearings: Snippets From Day 1." *Pharma Marketing Blog* (November 1, 2005) Retrieved Aug 21, 2023, from: http://pharmamkting.blogspot.com/2005/11/fda-dtc-hearings-snippets-from-day-1.html.

[84] Bremner, Doug: "When Should Children Be Given Antipsychotic Medications?" *Doug Bremner Personal Website* Accessed Sep 1, 2023, from:

https://www.dougbremner.com/topics/ADHD/when-should-children-be-given-antipsychotic-medications.html.

[85] Sniderman AD, Furberg CD: Why Guideline-Making Requires Reform. *JAMA*. 2009;301(4):429-431. doi:10.1001/jama.2009.15. Retrieved Aug 21, 2013, from: https://jamanetwork.com/journals/jama/article-abstract/183265.

[86] Godlee F: Doctors, patients, and the drug industry. *BMJ* 2009; 338:b463. doi: https://doi.org/10.1136/bmj.b463 (Published 05 February 2009). Retrieved Aug 5, 2023, from: https://www.bmj.com/content/338/bmj.b463.full.

[87] Gøtzsche PC: Breast screening: the facts—or maybe not. *BMJ* 2009; 338:b86. doi: https://doi.org/10.1136/bmj.b86. Published 28 January 2009. Retrieved July 22, 2023, from: https://www.bmj.com/content/338/bmj.b86.full.

[88] Neuhouser ML, Wassertheil-Smoller, S, Thomson C, et al: Multivitamin use and risk of cancer and cardiovascular disease in the Women's Health Initiative cohorts. *Arch Intern Med* 2009 Feb 9;169(3):294-304. doi: 10.1001/archinternmed.2008.540. DOI: 10.1001/archinternmed.2008.540. Retrieved July 22, 2023, from: https://pubmed.ncbi.nlm.nih.gov/19204221/.

[89] Gaziano JM, Glynn RJ, Christen WG, et al: Vitamins E and C in the prevention of prostate and total cancer in men: the Physicians' Health Study II randomized controlled trial. *JAMA* 2009 Jan 7;301(1):52-62. doi: 10.1001/jama.2008.862. Epub 2008 Dec 9. Retrieved on July 22, 2023, from: https://pubmed.ncbi.nlm.nih.gov/19066368/.

[90] Omenn GS, Goodman GE, Thornquist MD, et al. Effects of a combination of beta carotene and Vitamin A on lung cancer and cardiovascular disease. *The New England Journal of Medicine*. 1996;334(18):1150-1155. Retrieved July 22, 2023, from: https://pubmed.ncbi.nlm.nih.gov/8602180/.

[91] Feskanich D, Singh VB, Willett WC. Vitamin A intake and hip fracture among postmenopausal women. *JAMA* 2002; 287:47-54. Retrieved July 22, 2023, from: https://pubmed.ncbi.nlm.nih.gov/11754708/.

[92] Anon. "Denmark bans added vitamins in cereal." August 14, 2004, *The Sydney Morning Herald*. Retrieved July 22, 2023, from: https://www.smh.com.au/national/denmark-bans-added-vitamins-in-cereal-20040814-gdjjt1.html.

[93] ATBC. The Alpha-Tocopherol, Beta Carotene Cancer Prevention Study Group. The effect of vitamin E and beta carotene on the incidence of lung cancer and other cancers in male smokers. *The New England Journal of*

Medicine 1994; 330:1029-1035. Retrieved July 22, 2023, from: https://pubmed.ncbi.nlm.nih.gov/8127329/.

[94] Rapola JM, Virtamo J. Ripatti S, et al: Randomised trial of alpha-tocopherol and beta-carotene supplements on incidence of major coronary events in men with previous myocardial infarction. *Lancet* 1997; 349(9067):1715-1720. Retrieved July 22, 2023, from: https://pubmed.ncbi.nlm.nih.gov/9193380/.

[95] Vivekananthan DP, Penn MS, Sapp SK, Hsu A, Topol EJ. Use of antioxidant vitamins for the prevention of cardiovascular disease: Meta-analysis of randomised trials. *Lancet* 2003; 361(9374):2017-2023. doi:10.1016/S0140-6736(03)13637-9. Retrieved July 22, 2023, from: https://pubmed.ncbi.nlm.nih.gov/12814711/.

[96] Bjelakovic G, Nikolova D, Simonetti RG, Gluud C. Antioxidant supplements for prevention of gastrointestinal cancers: a systematic review and meta-analysis. *Lancet* 2004; 364:1219-1228. Retrieved July 22, 2023, from: https://pubmed.ncbi.nlm.nih.gov/15464182/.

[97] Waters DD, Alderman EL, Hsia J, et al. Effects of hormone replacement therapy and antioxidant vitamin supplements on coronary atherosclerosis in postmenopausal women: A randomized controlled trial. *JAMA* 2002;288(19):2432-2440. Retrieved July 22, 2023, from: https://pubmed.ncbi.nlm.nih.gov/12435256/.

[98] Brown BG, Zhao X-Q, Chait A, et al. Simvastatin and niacin, antioxidant vitamins, or the combination for the prevention of coronary disease. *The New England Journal of Medicine* 2001;345(22):1583-1592. Retrieved July 22, 2023, from: https://www.nejm.org/doi/full/10.1056/NEJMoa011090.

[99] Vivekananthan DP, Penn MS, Sapp SK, Hsu A, Topol EJ. Use of antioxidant vitamins for the prevention of cardiovascular disease: Meta-analysis of randomised trials. *Lancet* 2003; 361(9374):2017-2023. doi:10.1016/S0140-6736(03)13637-9. Retrieved July 22, 2023, from: https://pubmed.ncbi.nlm.nih.gov/12814711/.

[100] Bremner, Doug: "Herbs and Supplements for Weight Loss." *Doug Bremner Personal Website* Accessed Sep 1, 2023, from: https://www.dougbremner.com/topics/diet/herbs-and-supplements-for-weight-loss.html.

[101] Jefferson T, Di Pietrantonj C, Debalini MG, et al: Relation of study quality, concordance, take home message, funding, and impact in studies of influenza vaccines: systematic review. *BMJ* 2009; 338:b354 doi: https://doi.org/10.1136/bmj.b354 (Published 12 February 2009). Retrieved Aug 21, 2023, from: https://www.bmj.com/content/338/bmj.b354.

[102] Nutt DJ: Equasy — An overlooked addiction with implications for the current debate on drug harms. *Journal of Psychopharmacology* 2009;23(1):3-5. doi:10.1177/0269881108099672. Retrieved Aug 21, 2023, from: http://jop.sagepub.com/cgi/reprint/23/1/3.

[103] Staff: "Drugs advisor criticized by Smith." *BBC News* (9 February 2009) Retrieved Aug 21, 2023, from: http://news.bbc.co.uk/2/hi/uk_news/politics/7879378.stm.

[104] Pear, Robert: "U.S. to Compare Medical Treatments." *The New York Times* (February 15, 2009) Retrieved Aug 4, 2023, from: https://www.nytimes.com/2009/02/16/health/policy/16health.html?partner=rss&emc=rss.

[105] Pharmalittle: "Godzilla versus King Kong: FDA Preemption Meets Comparative Efficacy." *Pharmalittle* (February 16, 2009) Retrieved Aug 4, 2023, from: http://pharmalittle.blogspot.com/2009/02/comparative-efficacy-hoopla.html.

[106] Brody, Howard: "Big Government Want to Get Between You and Your Doctor: An Old Scare Tactic is Abroad in the Land." *Hooked: Ethics, Medicine, and Pharma* (February 16, 2009) Retrieved Aug 3, 2023, from: http://brodyhooked.blogspot.com/2009/02/big-goverment-wants-to-get-between-you.html

[107] Jaschick, Scott: "Double Standard at Emory?" *Inside Higher Ed* (June 30, 2009) Retrieved Aug 21, 2023, from: https://www.insidehighered.com/news/2009/07/01/double-standard-emory.

[108] Bonilla, Peter: "Emory professor allowed to say he's an Emory professor on private blog." *FIRE* (July 14, 2009) Retrieved Aug 21, 2023, from: https://www.thefire.org/news/emory-professor-allowed-say-hes-emory-professor-private-blog.

[109] Bremner, Anne and Doug Bremner: *Justice in the Age of Judgment: From Amanda Knox to Kyle Rittenhouse and the Battle for Due Process in the Digital Age* Skyhorse Publishing, 2022. Retrieved Aug 21, 2023, from: https://www.amazon.com/Amanda-Knox-Justice-Age-Judgment/dp/151075136X.

[110] Kindt M, Soeter M, Veryliet B: Beyond extinction: erasing human fear responses and preventing the return of fear. *Nature Neuroscience* 2009; 12:256–258. Retrieved Aug 21, 2023, from: https://pubmed.ncbi.nlm.nih.gov/19219038/.

[111] Pitman RK, Sanders KM, Zusman RM, et al. Pilot study of secondary prevention of posttraumatic stress disorder with propranolol. *Biol*

Psychiatry. 2002;51(2):189-192. Retrieved Aug 21, 2023, from: https://pubmed.ncbi.nlm.nih.gov/11822998/.

[112] Vaiva G, Ducrocq F, Jezequel K, et al. Immediate treatment with propranolol decreases posttraumatic stress disorder two months after trauma. *Biol Psychiatry* 2003;54(9):947-949. Retrieved Aug 21, 2023, from: https://pubmed.ncbi.nlm.nih.gov/14573324/.

[113] Cahill L, Prins B, Weber M, McGaugh JL. Beta-adrenergic activation and memory for emotional events. *Nature* 1994; 371:702-704. Retrieved Aug 21, 2023, from: https://pubmed.ncbi.nlm.nih.gov/7935815/.

[114] Bremner, Doug: "Can Changing Your Diet Help Your Depression?" *Doug Bremner Personal Website* Retrieved Aug 21, 2023, from: https://www.dougbremner.com/topics/depression/can-changing-diet-help-depression.html.

[115] Schwartz, Nelson D.: "Scoop Link: Fortune on Rumsfeld's Tamiflu $$$Mns." *Scoop* (October 31, 2005) Retrieved Aug 21, 2023, from: http://www.scoop.co.nz/stories/HL0511/S00036.htm.

[116] Ward P, Small I, Smith J, Suter P, Dutkowski R: Oseltamivir (Tamiflu®) and its potential for use in the event of an influenza pandemic. *Journal of Antimicrobial Chemotherapy* 2005; 55(suppl_1): i5-i21. February 2005, doi: 10.1093/jac/dki018 Retrieved Aug 21, 2023, from: http://jac.oxfordjournals.org/cgi/reprint/55/suppl_1/i5.pdf.

[117] Russell, Sabin: "Japan links Tamiflu to 2 teen suicides / 64 cases of disorders connected to avian flu treatment." *SFGate* (Nov. 18, 2005) Retrieved Aug 21, 2023, from: http://www.sfgate.com/cgi-bin/article.cgi?file=/c/a/2005/11/15/MNG29FO9K71.DTL.

[118] Kuehn BM: Long-term Risks of Bisphosphonates Probed. *JAMA* 2009;301(7):710-711. Retrieved Aug 21, 2023, from: http://jama.ama-assn.org/cgi/content/full/301/7/710.

[119] Lenart BA, Neviaser AS, Lyman S, et al: Association of low-energy femoral fractures with prolonged bisphosphonate use: a case control study. *Osteoporos Int* 2009; 20(8):1353-62. doi: 10.1007/s00198-008-0805-x. Epub 2008 Dec 9. Accessed Oct 1, 2023, from: https://pubmed.ncbi.nlm.nih.gov/19066707/.

[120] Bremner, Doug: "Should I Get My Bone Mineral Density (BMD) Checked?" *Doug Bremner Personal Website* Accessed Sep 1, 2023, from: https://www.dougbremner.com/topics/osteoporosis/should-i-get-my-bone-mineral-density-bmd-checked.html.

[121] Calabrese JR, Keck PE, Macfadden W, et al: A Randomized, Double-Blind, Placebo-Controlled Trial of Quetiapine in the Treatment of Bipolar I or II Depression. *The American Journal of Psychiatry* 2005; 162(7):1351-1360.

Doi: 10.1176/appi.ajp.162.7.1351. Retrieved Aug 21, 2023, from: https://ajp.psychiatryonline.org/doi/full/10.1176/appi.ajp.162.7.1351.

[122] Thase ME, Macfadden W, Weisler RH, et al: Efficacy of Quetiapine Monotherapy in Bipolar I and II Depression: A Double-blind, Placebo-controlled Study (The BOLDER II Study). *Journal of Clinical Psychopharmacology* 2006; 26(6):600-609. December 2006. doi: 10.1097/01.jcp.0000248603.76231.b7. Retrieved Aug 21, 2023, from: http://www.psychopharmacology.com/pt/re/jclnpsychopharm/abstract .00004714-200612000- 00009.htm;jsessionid=JmbGy4pVP46ttsq2CvCZ62JzRM9t4mGQpQTL2y7k 2QZ6GV1DsDvM!289474761!181195629!8091!-1.

[123] Carlat, Daniel: "Of Seroquel, Sex, and Secret Documents." *The Carlat Psychiatry Blog* (February 25, 2009) Retrieved Aug 21, 2023, from: https://carlatpsychiatry.blogspot.com/2009/02/of-seroquel-sex-and-secret-documents.html.

[124] Harris, Gardiner: "Crackdown on Doctors Who Take Kickbacks." *The New York* Times (March 3, 2009) Retrieved Aug 2, 2023, from: https://www.nytimes.com/2009/03/04/health/policy/04doctors.html?_r =1&scp=2&sq=gardiner%20harris&st=cse.

[125] Wilson, Duff: "Harvard Medical School in Ethics Quandary." *The New York* Times ((March 2, 2009) Retrieved Aug 2, 2023, from: https://www.nytimes.com/2009/03/03/business/03medschool.html?scp =1&sq=american%20medical%20student%20association&st=cse.

[126] Fiddaman, Bobbie: "Senator Charles Grassley Releases a Brochure from a GlaxoSmithKline Program Called Psychnet." *Fiddaman* Blog (March 5, 2009) Retrieved Aug 2, 2023, from: https://fiddaman.blogspot.com/2009/03/senator-charles-grassley-releases.html.

[127] Bremner JD, Vermetten E, Kelley ME: Cortisol, dehydroepiandrosterone, and estradiol measured over 24 hours in women with childhood sexual abuse-related posttraumatic stress disorder. *Journal of Nervous and Mental Disease* 2007; 195(11):919-927. https://pubmed.ncbi.nlm.nih.gov/18000454/

[128] Bremner JD, Fani N, Ashraf A, et al. Functional brain imaging alterations in acne patients treated with isotretinoin. *Am J Psychiatry* 2005; 162:983-991. Retrieved Aug 1, 2023, from: https://ajp.psychiatryonline.org/doi/full/10.1176/appi.ajp.162.5.983.

[129] Bremner JD, Fani N, et al: Correction: Functional brain imaging alterations in acne patients treated with isotretinoin. *The American Journal of Psychiatry* 162: 983-991

130 Bremner, Doug: "Herbs and Supplements for Menopausal Symptoms." *Doug Bremner Personal Website* Accessed Sep 1, 2023, from: https://www.dougbremner.com/topics/vitamins/herbs-and-supplements-for-menopausal-symptoms.html

131 Berger JS, Roncaglioni MC, Avanzini F, Pangrazzi I, Tognoni G, Brown DL (2006): Aspirin for the primary prevention of cardiovascular events in women and men: A sex-specific meta-analysis of randomized controlled trials. *Journal of the American Medical Association* 295:306-313. Retrieved Aug 23, 2023, from: https://pubmed.ncbi.nlm.nih.gov/16418466/.

132 ATC (2002): Antithrombotic Trialists' Collaboration: Collaborative meta-analysis of randomised trials of antiplatelet therapy for prevention of death, myocardial infarction, and stroke in high-risk patients. *British Medical Journal* 324:71-86. Retrieved Aug 23, 2023, from: https://pubmed.ncbi.nlm.nih.gov/11786451/.

133 Esprit (2006): Aspirin plus dipyridamole versus aspirin alone after cerebral ischaemia of arterial origin (ESPRIT): randomised controlled trial. The Lancet 367:1665-1673. Retrieved Aug 23, 2023, from: https://pubmed.ncbi.nlm.nih.gov/16714187/.

134 Bremner, Doug: "Do I Have an Ulcer or is it Just Gastroesophageal Reflux Disease?" *Doug Bremner Personal Website Accessed* Sep 1, 2023, from: https://www.dougbremner.com/topics/GI/do-i-have-an-ulcer-or-is-it-just-gerd.html.

135 Tricoci P, Allen JM, Kramer JM, Califf RM, Smith SC: Scientific Evidence Underlying the ACC/AHA Clinical Practice Guidelines. *JAMA* 2009;301(8):831-841. doi:10.1001/jama.2009.205. Retrieved Aug 23, 2023, from: http://jama.ama-assn.org/cgi/content/full/301/8/831.

136 Cockcroft, Lucy: "UK psychiatrist Tonmoy Sharma is struck off." *The Telegraph* (01 April 2008) Retrieved Aug 23, 2023, from: http://www.telegraph.co.uk/news/uknews/1583475/BBC-psychiatrist-Tonmoy-Sharma-is-struck-off.html.

137 Whang W, Kubzansky LD, Kawachi I, et al. Depression and risk of sudden cardiac death and coronary heart disease in women: Results of the Nurses' Heart Study. *J Am Coll Cardiol* 2009; 53:950-958. Retrieved Aug 23, 2023, from: https://pubmed.ncbi.nlm.nih.gov/19281925/.

138 Narayan SM, Stein MB: Do Depression or Antidepressants Increase Cardiovascular Mortality? The Absence of Proof Might Be More Important Than the Proof of Absence. *Journal of the American College of Cardiology* 2009 Mar; 53(11):959–961. Retrieved Aug 23, 2023, from: https://www.jacc.org/doi/10.1016/j.jacc.2008.12.009.

[139] Shaneyfelt TM, Centor RM: Reassessment of clinical practice guidelines: Go gently into that good night. *JAMA* 2009; 301(8):868-869. Retrieved Aug 2, 2023, from: https://pubmed.ncbi.nlm.nih.gov/19244197/.

[140] Andriole GL, Crawford ED, Grubb RL, et al: Mortality results from a randomized prostate-cancer screening trial. *New Engl J Med* 2009; 360(13):1310-9. doi: 10.1056/NEJMoa0810696. Epub 2009 Mar 18. Retrieved July 22, 2023, from: https://pubmed.ncbi.nlm.nih.gov/19297565/.

[141] Schröder FH, Hugosson J, Roobol MJ, et al: The European Randomized Study of Screening for Prostate Cancer – Prostate Cancer Mortality at 13 Years of Follow-up. *Lancet* 2014 Dec 6; 384(9959): 2027–2035.
Published online 2014 Aug 6. doi: 10.1016/S0140-6736(14)60525-0. Retrieved July 22, 2023, from: https://www.ncbi.nlm.nih.gov/pmc/articles/PMC4427906/.

[142] Bremner, Doug: "When Do I Need to Go to the Doctor For My Enlarged Prostate?" *Doug Bremner Personal Website* Accessed Sep 1, 2023, from: https://www.dougbremner.com/topics/bph/when-do-i-need-to-go-to-the-doctor-for-my-enlarged-prostate.html.

[143] Schroder FH, et al: Screening and prostate cancer mortality: results of the European Randomised Study of Screening for Prostate Cancer (ERSPC) at 13 years of follow-up. *Lancet* 2014 December 6; 384(9959): 2027–2035. doi:10.1016/S0140-6736(14)60525-0). Accessed Oct 1, 2023, from: https://pubmed.ncbi.nlm.nih.gov/25108889/.

[144] He FJ, MacGregor GA: A comprehensive review on salt and health and current experience of worldwide salt reduction programmes. *J Hum Hypertens* 2009 Jun; 23(6):363-84. doi: 10.1038/jhh.2008.144. Epub 2008 Dec 25. PMID: 19110538. Retrieved Aug 23, 2023, from: https://pubmed.ncbi.nlm.nih.gov/19110538/.

[145] Bremner, Doug: "Getting Blood Pressure Under Control Without Medications." *Doug Bremner Personal Website Accessed* Sep 1, 2023, from: https://www.dougbremner.com/topics/hypertension/getting-blood-pressure-under-control-without-medications.html

[146] Editorial: "PTSD and the Purple Heart." *The New York Times* ((Jan 11, 2009) Retrieved Aug 23, 2023, from: http://www.nytimes.com/2009/01/12/opinion/12mon2.html.

[147] Alvarez, Lizette, and Erik Eckholm: "Purple Heart Ruled Out for Traumatic Stress." *The New York Times* (Jan 7, 2009) Retrieved Aug 23, 2023, from: http://www.nytimes.com/2009/01/08/us/08purple.html?fta=y.

[148] Dobbs, David: "Soldier's Stress: What Doctors Get Wrong About PTSD." *Scientific American* (April 1, 2009) Retrieved Aug 23, 2023, from: http://www.sciam.com/article.cfm?id=post-traumatic-stress-trap.

[149] Spitzer R, First MB, Wakefield JC: Saving PTSD from itself in DSM-V. *J Anxiety Disord* 2007;21(2):233-41. doi: 10.1016/j.janxdis.2006.09.006. Epub 2006 Dec 1. PMID: 17141468 DOI: 10.1016/j.janxdis.2006.09.006

[150] Abelson, Reed: "A Healthcare Plan for All and the Concerns It Raises." *The New York Times* (March 24, 2009) Retrieved Aug 4, 2023, from: https://www.nytimes.com/2009/03/25/health/policy/25medicare.html?_r=1&scp=2&sq=%20health%20insurance&st=cse.

[151] Pear, Robert: "Insurers Offer to Soften a Key Rate Setting Policy." *The New York Times* (March 24, 2009) Retrieved Aug 3, 2023, from: https://www.nytimes.com/2009/03/25/health/policy/25health.html?scp=7&sq=healthcare&st=cse.

[152] Brody, Howard: "Psychiatrists Get Religion, To a Degree." *Hooked: Ethics, Medicine, and Pharma* (March 25, 2009) Retrieved Aug 5, 2023, from: http://brodyhooked.blogspot.com/2009/03/psychiatrists-get-religion-to-degree.html

[153] Cayce, Edgar. *There is a River*. Retrieved Aug 23, 2023, from: https://www.amazon.com/Story-Edgar-Cayce-There-River/dp/0876043759.

[154] Jolles S, Sewell WA, Leighton C: Drug-induced aseptic meningitis: diagnosis and management. *Drug Saf* 2000 Mar;22(3):215-26. doi: 10.2165/00002018-200022030-00005. PMID: 10738845 doi: 10.2165/00002018-200022030-00005. Retrieved Aug 2, 2023, from: https://pubmed.ncbi.nlm.nih.gov/10738845/.

[155] HistoryLink Staff: "Group Health Cooperative Olympia Medical Center Opens on July 1, 1972." *HistoryLink.org* (January 25, 2006) Retrieved Aug 23, 2023, from: https://www.historylink.org/File/7627.

[156] Staff: "William Bremner MD PhD Stepping Down as Chair After Twenty Years." *UW Med News* (April 26, 2016) Retrieved Aug 23, 2023, from: https://mednews.uw.edu/news/bremner-stepping-down.

[157] Bremner, J. Douglas: *Before You Take That Pill: Why the Drug Industry May Be Bad For Your Health: Risks and Side Effects You Won't Find on the Label of Commonly Prescribed Medications, Vitamins and Supplements.* Avery/Penguin. 2008. Retrieved Aug 23, 2023, from: https://www.amazon.com/Before-You-Take-that-Pill/dp/1583332952

[158] Roizen, Michael and Mehmet Oz: *YOU: The Owner's Manual*. WilliamMr, 2005. Retrieved Aug 23, 2023, from: http://www.amazon.com/YOU-Owners-Insiders-Healthier-Younger/dp/0060765313.

[159] Clifford, Stephanie: "Online Age Quiz is a Window for Drug Makers." *The New York Times* (March 25, 2009) Retrieved Aug 23, 2023, from:

http://www.nytimes.com/2009/03/26/technology/internet/26privacy.html.

[160] Bremner, Doug: "What Causes High Blood Pressure?" *Doug Bremner Personal Website* Accessed Sep 1, 2023, from: https://www.dougbremner.com/topics/hypertension/what-causes-high-blood-pressure.html

[161] He FJ, MacGregor GA: A comprehensive review on salt and health and current experience of worldwide salt reduction programmes. *J Hum Hypertens* 2009 Jun; 23(6):363-84. doi: 10.1038/jhh.2008.144. Epub 2008 Dec 25. PMID: 19110538. Retrieved Aug 23, 2023, from: https://pubmed.ncbi.nlm.nih.gov/19110538/.

[162] Bremner, Doug: "Does Saw Palmetto Help Enlarged Prostate?" *Doug Bremner Personal Website* Accessed Sep 1, 2023, from: https://www.dougbremner.com/topics/vitamins/does-saw-palmetto-help-enlarged-prostate.html

[163] Skloot, Rebecca: "Lap-Dance Science." *The New York Times Magazine* (Dec. 9, 2007) Retrieved Aug 7, 2023, from: https://www.nytimes.com/2007/12/09/magazine/09lapdance.html?_r=1&oref=slogin.

[164] Bremner, Doug: "Are Birth Control Pills Safe?" *Doug Bremner Personal Website* Retrieved Aug 5, 2023, from: https://www.dougbremner.com/topics/sexuality_reproduction/are-birth-control-pills-safe.html.

[165] Freedman, R., et al: Conflict of interest – An issue for every psychiatrist. *Am J Psychiatry.* 2009 Mar; 166(3): 274. doi: 10.1176/appi.ajp.2009.09010093. Retrieved Aug 1, 2023, from: https://www.ncbi.nlm.nih.gov/pmc/articles/PMC4430107/.

[166] Carlat, Daniel: "Psychiatry's Leadership is Getting Real." *The Carlat Psychiatry Blog* (March 5, 2009) Retrieved Aug 4, 2023. From: http://carlatpsychiatry.blogspot.com/2009/03/psychiatrys-leadership-is-getting-real.html

[167] Brody, Howard: "Psychiatry: Looking in the Mirror?" *Hooked: Ethics, Medicine, and Pharma* (March 11, 2009) Retrieved Aug 4, 2023, from: http://brodyhooked.blogspot.com/2009/03/psychiatry-looking-in-mirror.html

[168] Bremner JD, Fani N, Ashraf A, et al. Functional brain imaging alterations in acne patients treated with isotretinoin. *Am J Psychiatry* 2005; 162:983-991. Retrieved Aug 1, 2023, from: https://ajp.psychiatryonline.org/doi/full/10.1176/appi.ajp.162.5.983.

[169169] Vedantam, Shankar: "Debate Over Drugs for ADHD Reignites." *The Washington Post* (March 27, 2009) Retrieved Aug 23, 2023, from: http://www.washingtonpost.com/wp-dyn/content/article/2009/03/26/AR2009032604018.html.
[170] Molina BSG, Hinshaw SP, Swanson LM, et al: The MTA at 8 Years: Prospective Follow-Up of Children Treated for Combined Type ADHD in a Multisite Study. *J Am Acad Child Adolesc Psychiatry* 2009 May; 48(5): 484–500. doi: 10.1097/CHI.0b013e31819c23d0. PMCID: PMC3063150. PMID: 19318991.
Retrieved Aug 23, 2023, from: https://www.ncbi.nlm.nih.gov/pmc/articles/PMC3063150/.
[171] Pelham WE, Burrows-Maclean L, Gnagy EM, et al: Transdermal methylphenidate, behavioral, and combined treatment for children with ADHD. *Exp Clin Psychopharmacol* 2005 May;13(2):111-26.
doi: 10.1037/1064-1297.13.2.111. PMID: 15943544 DOI: 10.1037/1064-1297.13.2.111 Retrieved Aug 23, 2023, from: https://pubmed.ncbi.nlm.nih.gov/15943544/
[172] Jensen PS, Arnold LE, Swanson JM, et al. 3-year follow-up of the NIMH MTA study. *J Am Acad Child Adolesc Psychiatry* 2007 Aug;46(8):989-1002. doi: 10.1097/CHI.0b013e3180686d48. PMID: 17667478 doi: 10.1097/CHI.0b013e3180686d48. Retrieved Aug 23, 2023, from https://pubmed.ncbi.nlm.nih.gov/17667478/.
[173] Pelham WE, Burrows-Maclean L, Gnagy EM, et al: Transdermal methylphenidate, behavioral, and combined treatment for children with ADHD. *Exp Clin Psychopharmacol* 2005 May;13(2):111-26.
doi: 10.1037/1064-1297.13.2.111. PMID: 15943544 DOI: 10.1037/1064-1297.13.2.111 Retrieved Aug 23, 2023, from: https://pubmed.ncbi.nlm.nih.gov/15943544/
[174] Pelham WE, Fabiano GA, et al: Treatment Sequencing for Childhood ADHD: A Multiple-Randomization Study of Adaptive Medication and Behavioral Interventions. *J Clin Child Adolescent Psychol* 2016; 45(4):396-415. doi: 10.1080/15374416.2015.1105138. Accessed Nov 4, 2023, from: https://pubmed.ncbi.nlm.nih.gov/26882332.
[175] Clinpsych: "The Vioxx Hit Squad." *Clinical Psychiatry and Psychology: A Closer Look.* (April 1, 2009) Retrieved Aug 23, 2023, from: http://clinpsyc.blogspot.com/2009/04/vioxx-hit-squad.html
[176] Langs, Robert: *Rating Your Psychotherapist* Henry Holt & Co. (1988) Retrieved Aug 23, 2023, from: http://www.amazon.com/Rating-Your-Psychotherapist-Whether-

Therapy/dp/B000JZUDVC/ref=sr_1_1?ie=UTF8&s=books&qid =1237950027&sr=8-1.

[177] Dinah, ClinkShrink & Roy: "To Sleep, Perchance to Dream..." *Shrink Rap* (February 3, 2009) Retrieved Aug 23, 2023, from http://psychiatrist-blog.blogspot.com/2009/02/to-sleep-perchance-to-dream.html.

[178] 2. Davis BR. Major cardiovascular events in hypertensive patients randomized to doxazosin versus chlorthalidone: The Antihypertensive and Lipid-Lowering Treatment to Prevent Heart Attack Trial (ALLHAT). *J Am Med Assoc.* 2000; 283:1967-1975. Retrieved Sep 12,2023, from: https://pubmed.ncbi.nlm.nih.gov/10789664/.

[179] Bremner, Doug: "Prescription Medications for the Treatment of Hypertension." *Doug Bremner Personal Website* accessed Sep 12,2023, from: https://www.dougbremner.com/topics/hypertension/prescription-medications-for-the-treatment-of-hypertension.html.

[180] MikeHansonArchive: "Aspartame Killed My Wife – One Man's Story." *YouTube* Retrieved Aug 23, 2023, from: http://www.youtube.com/v/_rJ1jpr5c4Y&hl=en&fs=1.

[181] Moynihan, Ray, and Alan Cassels: *Selling Sickness: How the World's Largest Drug Companies are Turning Us All into Patients.* Bold Type Books, 2006. Accessed Oct 1, 2023, from: https://www.amazon.com/Selling-Sickness-Pharmaceutical-Companies-Patients/dp/156025856X.

[182] Lidz, Theodore and Stephen Fleck: *Schizophrenia and the Family* Intl Universities Press, 1985. Retrieved Aug 23, 2023, from: http://www.amazon.com/dp/082366001X.

[183] 183 Cyrulnik, Boris: *Resilience* Penguin, 2009. Retrieved Aug 23, 2023, from: http://www.amazon.de/Resilience-Your-Inner-Strength-Free/dp/product-description/014103615X.

[184] Holmes, Hannah: *The Well-Dressed Ape* Random House, 2009. Retrieved Aug 23, 2023, from: http://www.amazon.com/Well-Dressed-Ape-Natural-History-Myself/dp/1400065410.